The Science of
Adhesive Joints

The Science of
Adhesive Joints

J. J. BIKERMAN

Massachusetts Institute of Technology
Cambridge, Massachusetts

1961 (AP)

ACADEMIC PRESS
New York and London

ACADEMIC PRESS INC.
111 FIFTH AVENUE
NEW YORK 3, N. Y.

United Kingdom Edition
Published by
ACADEMIC PRESS INC. (LONDON) LTD.
17 OLD QUEEN STREET, LONDON SW 1

Library of Congress Catalog Card Number 60-16906

Preface

Some sciences were born and bred in laboratories; consequently, their development was almost logical and their advance consisted in adding new, more than in rejecting old, concepts and observations. The science of radioactivity is a suitable example of this class.

The science of adhesive joints belongs to the opposite type. The art of making adhesive bonds is older than are physics and chemistry, and a large number of disconnected ideas, rules, and traditions has been accumulated by the many generations familiar with adhesives. In such an instance, the first task of a monograph writer is to remove the chaff and to expose the grains. This was attempted in the present volume.

The (presumably) most fundamental alternative to be decided can be explained by referring to the well-known field of medicine. There are diseases which are caused by the *presence* of unwanted organisms (these are the infectious diseases), and there are diseases produced by the *absence* of wanted ingredients (these are the deficiency diseases occurring when the vitamin intake is insufficient). If an adhesive joint is weak, is weakness present or is strength absent? The tradition leaned toward the latter opinion; it was believed that the breaking stress of an adhesive joint was small when the molecular forces between the adherend and the adhesive were not strong enough. We now prefer the former alternative; when a joint is weak and breaks apparently in adhesion, a weak boundary layer is likely to be present. It is hoped that attentive readers of this book will be converted to our creed.

The word Science is included in the title of this book to avoid misleading potential users into expecting ready-made formulations for producing adhesives or adhesive joints. I believe, and experience confirms this belief, that the new science of adhesive joints is eminently practical; but it has to be intelligently applied to bring practical results. The last chapter of the book is intended to indicate how such an application should be attempted. Neither this nor any other chapter contains recommended adhesive compositions or recommended designs of the bond.

I took the liberty of inventing a new word: *adhint* as an abbreviation for *adhesive joint*. This portmanteau word is explained in the text and also listed in the subject index, and I hope that not many readers will be puzzled or annoyed by it.

The book was written when the author's laboratory was supported by grants from Lord Manufacturing Company of Erie, Pennsylvania; Allied Chemical Company of New York, N. Y.; Owens-Corning Fiberglas Corporation of Ashton, Rhode Island; and the National Science Foundation. I am deeply grateful to all these organizations.

The help given to me by Professors A. G. H. Dietz and F. J. McGarry of M.I.T. was invaluable.

J. J. BIKERMAN

November 1960

Contents

CHAPTER 1

Solid Surfaces

Why Adhesives Are Needed

§1. IF A SOLID, such as a glass rod, is broken and the newly formed ends are brought together, the initial solid is not restored. We are so used to this common phenomenon that we do not pause to think it over, but it is striking and its explanation explains also why adhesives are used at all.[1]

The irrevocability of rupture is remarkable because the interatomic and intermolecular forces known to us are conservative forces, that is their magnitude does not depend on the past history of the system. If the atoms in the intact glass rod attracted each other so strongly that a considerable force was required to separate them, an equal force ought to be needed when the rupture surfaces are again pressed against each other. In reality, of course, the mutual attraction of the two fragments is almost zero. The discrepancy is due to two reasons, namely surface roughness and boundary layers.

The rupture surfaces are rough. Because of the insufficient steadiness of our hands and tools it would be impossible to fit every hill of one surface exactly in the corresponding valley on the opposite surface, even if such a correspondence existed. However, as practically every solid exhibits some plasticity before it breaks, or stresses in it are relieved during fracture, a hill torn out of surface B and now being a part of surface A has a shape different from that of the valley remaining in surface B; thus no perfect fit would be achieved even by an absolutely precise guide.

When a solid is broken in any medium except an extraordinarily good vacuum, the two fracture surfaces very rapidly become covered with adsorbed molecules. In atmospheric air,

1

water is the main substance "physically" adsorbed, see §12. In addition, air which we inhale contains numerous particles larger than a molecule; they also settle on every freshly exposed surface. Thus on the fracture surfaces, contrary to the testimony of the unaided eye, no atoms of the glass are exposed. When these surfaces are mutually pressed, there is no glass-to-glass contact. Moist air is present everywhere between the two glass bodies, and the thickness of the air film varies from point to point on the surface; at some spots the two adsorbed layers are in contact and only a few (perhaps only two) foreign molecules keep the solids apart, while at other points the clearance between the solids may be a million times as great.

An adhesive has to counteract the effects of surface roughness and boundary layers. It has to fill the valleys and to remove surface impurities. If it does this, a continuous contact between the solids (often called *adherends*) and the adhesive is established, and the new three-layer solid (consisting of adherend-adhesive-adherend) has a notable strength.

Transition Layers Rather Than Surfaces

§2. PROPERTIES of solid surfaces influence a host of important phenomena and ought to be generally known. As, however, experience shows that the nature of solid surfaces is very often misunderstood and that this misunderstanding is an obstinate obstacle to approving a logical concept of *adhints* (= adhesive joints, abbreviated), a condensed review of solid surfaces must be given here.

At a zero-order approximation, solid surfaces are geometrical planes (having no thickness) separating two homogeneous phases. This approximation is unsatisfactory for any but the crudest experiments. In reality, transition layers rather than surfaces exist on every solid. Figure 1 schematically represents a cross section of a typical transition layer. The top part is air. The density and composition of the gas phase a few angstroms from the solid are affected by the solid; this effect belongs to adsorption, and adsorbed gas is denoted by dots in the graph. Often,

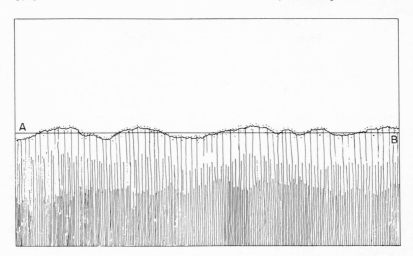

Fig. 1. Cross section of a typical solid surface. The solid is shaded, and gradation of shading indicates gradual change of properties on nearing the interface with air (white). The dots are adsorbed molecules.

some molecules penetrate into the solid lattice and may be said to be dissolved in it; they are shown as dots among the dashes.

The bottom part of the figure is the solid. The densely shaded lowest portion of it has the properties of the material in bulk. The graded shading toward the interface is intended to convey the idea that the change in the properties of the solid from the middle to the interface is gradual.

If the hills on the surface were rased and used to fill the valleys, the interface would have been a plane, shown in the figure by the straight line AB. This plane usually is referred to as the *main plane* of the surface.

Surface Roughness

§3. IF THE GEOMETRICAL surface represented by line AB in Fig. 1 is curved, the true surface is said to have waviness in addition to roughness. If the former surface is plane, the latter is only rough.

Surface roughness (also known as *rugosity*) can be expressed
in many different forms. An exaggerated profile of the surface,
exemplified by graph 2, is a striking representation. The curves
of Fig. 2 were obtained by dragging a thin needle, whose tip was
a hemisphere of 13 microns (= 0.0013 cm.) radius, over metal
surfaces and magnifying the displacements of the needle. The
instruments used for these tests are called profilometers, surface
analyzers, and so on. The magnification in the direction of the
main plane is much smaller (for instance, in the ratio 1:13000
in the figure) than in the perpendicular direction, thus simulating
nonexistent sharp peaks on the surface; since, however, the
magnifications are known, the actual outline can be deduced

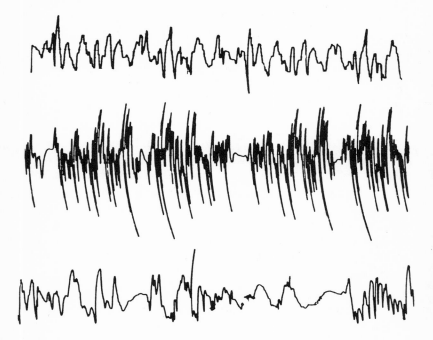

FIG. 2. Stylus curves of two metal surfaces; vertical magnification about
40,000, horizontal magnification about 3.3. Upper curve: stainless steel No.
302, Finish No. 4. Middle curve: nickel, nominal roughness 3 microinches.
Lower curve: same nickel surface examined in a perpendicular direction.

from the curves, and this actual profile often resembles that shown in Fig. 1.

If an area A of the solid has been explored by a tracer needle (also called stylus), the vertical distance (that is, perpendicular to the main plane) between the highest peak and the deepest valley over this area is h_{max}. Naturally the value of h_{max} increases with A. The height of the tallest peak above the main plane often is not very different from $0.5\ h_{max}$. If the height of the true surface above the main plane has been determined for n points and was found to be h_1, h_2, $\cdots$ h_n, then

$$(1/n)(h_1 + h_2 + \cdots h_n) = h_{av}$$

is the average height of elevations. The average depth of valleys also is equal to h_{av}. The root-mean-square deviation from the main plane is directly given by some instruments on the market; it is

$$h_{rms} = [(1/n)(h_1^2 + h_2^2 + \cdots h_n^2)]^{1/2}$$

and the values of h are determined along both hills and valleys. For a profile which can be represented as a sum of sinusoids, $h_{rms} = 1.11\ h_{av}$.

§4.   IF THE LENGTH of the boundary line as shown in Fig. 1 is z times the length of the straight line AB, then the actual area of the interface (assumed to be isotropic) is z^2 times the geometrical area. The measurement of true surface areas has been performed on powdered or porous solids more often than on bars, plates, etc. However, a few methods are available also for measuring z^2 of adherends.

If, for instance, a piece of metal M is immersed in a solution containing a radioactive isotope of M (in the form of ions), and the activity of the metal is determined from time to time, it is found that this activity rapidly rises in the first few seconds or minutes of contact but later remains almost stationary. The amount rapidly taken up is equal to that amount of M which is present so near to the solution that it can react with the liquid without intervening slow diffusion processes. Suppose that this amount is m grams for 1 cm.² of the geometrical surface. If the volume of one gram of the metal is v_0 cm.^{3}/g., the volume exchanged is mv_0 cm.^{3}. When spread in a film one atom thick, this volume would cover $mv_0{}^{2/3}N^{1/3}$ cm.^{2}, if N is the number of atoms in the gram (i.e., Avogadro number/atomic weight). If the penetration of radioactive atoms into the metal lattice, see §2, and similar complications are disregarded, then $z^2 = mv_0{}^{2/3}N^{1/3}$.

Another method requires electrochemical equipment. According to the accepted theory of the electric double layer at a metal-solution boundary, the capacity of this layer is independent of the nature of the metal and is determined above all by the nature of the solution and by the difference between the actual potential ψ of the metal and its zero-charge potential ψ_0 in the same solution. Thus, if the capacity of a mercury-solution interface is measured and found to be C_0 microfarads per cm.^{2} at a definite $\psi - \psi_0$, and then, in an identical solution and at the identical value of $\psi - \psi_0$, the capacity of a solid electrode proves to be C_1 microfarads for one square centimeter of the geometrical surface (or of the main plane, §2), then the true area of the solid is approximately C_1/C_0 times its geometrical area, as liquid mercury has a smooth surface. One of the methods of finding C_0 and C_1 employs very weak direct currents. The electrode (either of mercury or a solid) is cathodically polarized with a current density of, say, 10^{-6} amp. for cm.^{2} of the geometrical surface. This current brings, in t sec., $10^{-6}t$ coulomb of charge to each cm.^{2} of the surface. The potential of the metal against a reference electrode is measured during this charge. Let $\psi_2 - \psi_1$ be the change in this potential caused by the approach of $10^{-6}t$ coulomb. If both $\psi_2 - \psi_1$ and $\frac{1}{2}(\psi_2 - \psi_1) - \psi_0$ are made identical for the solid and the liquid electrode, then $z^2 = t_1/t_0$, if t_1 is the duration of charging for the solid metal, and t_0 is that for mercury. The main difficulty of the method resides in the necessity to avoid any passage of current across the metal-solution boundary; thus, the solution should not contain easily dischargeable metal ions, oxygen, and so on.

The method of calculating z^2, based on the adsorption of gases or solutes, is referred to in §§12 and 13.

§5.   A VALUE almost identical with h_{av} is found by determining the thickness of the "stagnant" layer of liquid on a rough surface. The experiment consists in moistening the surface (e.g., of a plate) with an excess of a nonvolatile liquid, suspending the plate vertically so that its bottom edge touches a bibulous pad (filter paper or unglazed porcelain), and weighing the plate with the remaining liquid from time to time. It is found that the liquid drains down as if a layer of it, H_0 cm. thick, did not participate in the motion. This H_0 in the author's experiments[2] was nearly equal to the h_{rms}, as illustrated in Table I.

TABLE I

THICKNESS OF "STAGNANT" LAYER (H_0) AND HEIGHT OF ELEVATIONS (h_{rms}) ON STAINLESS STEEL SURFACES. VACUUM OIL

	H_0 microns	h_{rms} microns
Surface finish No. 1	2.9 –3.6	3.15–3.83
No. 2D small	0.84–1.1	0.91–0.94
No. 2D large	0.52	0.28
No. 2B small	0.22–0.54	0.17–0.33
No. 2B large	0.26	0.12

A somewhat related procedure permits an estimate of h_{max}. An optical flat, that is a glass disc whose plane faces are flat within about ±0.1 micron, is pressed against a flat but rough solid surface on which beforehand a droplet of an oil has been deposited. The droplet is squashed and now occupies an area A; the outline of this area usually is visible to the unaided eye. If the volume of the droplet is v, the h_{max} of the solid is approximately equal to $2v/A$. This is explained by Fig. 3. The optical flat (near the top of the figure) rests on a few hills of the solid surface (A and B are shown). If the main plane is represented

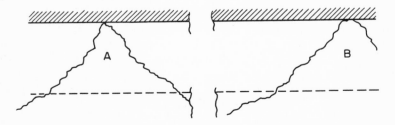

FIG. 3. Contact of a very smooth and a very rough surface.

by the dotted line, it is clear that $0.5\,h_{max}$ is the distance between this plane and the optical flat. On the other hand, the
volume occupied by the liquid is $0.5\,Ah_{max}$ because the volume
of hills rising above the main plane is approximately compensated by the volume of the valleys below this plane.

Another value related to h_{max} is determined with gas leakage
instruments. Figure 4 demonstrates the principle of these instruments. A metal or glass tube A with a well-polished end
surface is placed on the rough surface B, and air (or another
gas) is forced along the tube. Since there are air passages between the hills on B, air escapes along the surface of B, and from
the rate of this escape at a given overpressure in the tube the
average clearance between A and B and thus the height of the
few highest hills on B can be computed.

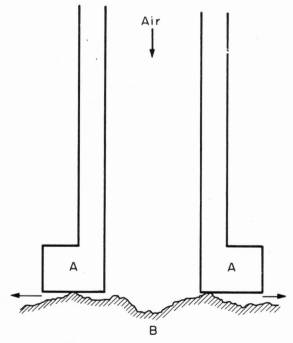

FIG. 4. A pneumatic roughness meter. The rate of flow of air depends on
the height of hills on the test surface B.

Friction phenomena afford valuable information on surface roughness.

As long as "the law of friction" (Leonardo da Vinci, Amontons, Coulomb) is valid for sliding, that is as long as frictional force F is independent of the area of contact and proportional to the normal load F_n, the coefficient of friction $\mu(=F/F_n)$ is equal to the tangent of the "effective slope" which cannot be significantly different from the average slope of a few tallest hills on the rubbing surfaces. The most frequent values of μ are confined to the region 0.1 to 0.5. Since 0.1 is approximately equal to tan 6° and 0.5 to tan 27°, this means that the most common hills on usual surfaces have slopes between 6° and 27°, which well accords with the data supplied, for instance, by tracer instruments, §3.

The conventional coefficient of rolling friction (contrary to the coefficient of sliding friction which is a pure number) is a length; it is defined as $\chi = Fr/F_n$, r being the radius of the rolling sphere. For small values of F_n and rough surfaces, this coefficient is approximately equal to twice the distance between hills so tall that the sphere can rest on them. The approximate height h of these hills is given by the equation $h = \chi^2/2r$. This h should be nearer to h_{max} than to h_{av}.

When a liquid drop slides along a tilted plate which is poorly wetted by the liquid, the product $F_n \cdot \sin \alpha/w$ is independent of the drop dimensions. F_n is the weight of the drop, w is its width during the sliding, and α is the tilt at which sliding proceeds without deceleration or acceleration. This product is greater the greater the rugosity of the plate.[3] A quantitative correlation between a geometrical parameter of surface roughness (such as h_{max} or h_{rms}) and the value of $F_n \cdot \sin \alpha/w$ has not been established yet. See also §21.

§6.   THE IMPORTANCE of waviness for adhesive joints is commented on in §37. There exists a stylus-type instrument[4] which determines both waviness and rugosity in one operation, but usually estimation of waviness is based on optical measurements. An optical flat is placed on the surface of an adherend. If, after a slight wringing, the whole adherend-glass interface acquires one color, the adherend is as flat as the glass plate. Usually, however, the interface will exhibit one or a few sets of interference fringes. The clearance between the glass and the adherend increases (for normal incidence) by half the wavelength (that is approximately 0.25 micron in daylight) from one to the next fringe. Suppose, for instance, that only one set of fringes is visible and that it forms concentric rings around the middle of the adherend surface. If n is the number of the rings, we may conclude that the air gap between the two solids is about $0.25n$ micron thicker (or, rarely, thinner) at the edge that in the center; in other words, the adherend is curved so that its highest point is $0.25n$ micron higher than the lowest. If this surface is convex toward the air, the interference fringes move out (or the concentric rings become greater) if the two solids are more strongly pressed together.

Optical methods often are used for determination or estimation of roughness also.

Interferometric procedures give results most easily correlated with the geometry of the surface. Let an optical flat be placed on the adherend whose main plane, §2, also is perfectly flat. Then the glass disc rests on a few (at least three) tallest hills, and the thickness of the air gap at any point depends on the height of the hills and the depth of the valleys which face each other at this point; see Fig. 5. Consequently the interference fringes will have an irregular pattern, and from this pattern the distribution of protuberances and depressions on the two surfaces can be derived. A better vertical resolution is achieved by multiple interferometry,[5] and a better horizontal resolution is attained in microinterferometers.[6] The first of these improvements permits one to notice and measure the height of lower hills and the

Fig. 5. Clearance between two solids.

depth of more shallow valleys, while the second renders possible
the recording of sharper peaks, more narrow ridges, finer cracks,
and similar features whose extension along the main plane is too
small for the naked eye.

The reflectivity of a surface is well suited for a qualitative
estimate of its roughness. If it does not reflect light as a mirror
does, we may be sure that it has many irregularities exceeding
the wavelength of the light used, that is its h_{av} must be at least
0.5 micron. If the surface does have a mirror finish, it still can
have (and usually has) hills and valleys of this and greater dimensions, but they are not easily visible because of the high intensity
of the light reflected in the specular fashion.

A quantitative information on the rugosity of a surface is
obtained when the intensity of the reflected light is measured as
a function of the angle of reflection. If a parallel beam of light,
see Fig. 6, falls on a surface containing facets inclined at different
angles to the main plane, the reflected light is divergent instead
of being parallel, and from the intensity of the radiation reflected, for instance, parallel to direction BC the area covered
with facets parallel to MN can be calculated. If the intensity of
the beam parallel to EF (that is, reflected from NO which is
parallel to the main plane) is n times that of the beam parallel
to BC, then the area of the surfaces parallel to MN is $1/n$th
that of the surfaces parallel to the main plane. Analogous calcu-

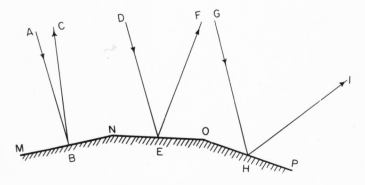

Fig. 6. Reflection of light from a rough surface.

lations have been made also for surfaces covered with circular buttons or depressions;[7] the latter type is obtained, for instance, by sandblasting.

An easy and often excellent method of estimating surface roughness is simply looking at it in a microscope, especially when the surface is obliquely illuminated. Irregularities as small as one micron in the shortest dimension often can be noticed. There are special microscopes on the market which permit one to see two surfaces (a test object and a standard plate) next to each other and thus to decide whether their rugosities are or are not similar.

Absorption of electrons is often resorted to for the determination of the topography of a solid surface in a slightly devious way. In Fig. 7 the shaded part represents the object of study.

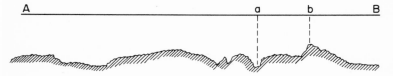

FIG. 7. Replica method of estimating surface roughness.

It is coated with another material (a "replica") which, according to the circumstances, may be a thermoplastic polymer, or silica, or something else. This material should have the property of filling all depressions on the solid and of giving a very smooth surface at the opposite side of the coating (that is, AB should be as straight as possible). Then the coating film is removed from the solid; this can be achieved by stripping or, when permissible, by dissolving the solid away. It is postulated that the film is not distorted during this process. Finally, the coating is placed in an electron microscope. The electrons cross it normally to the main plane of the film. Evidently, fewer electrons will be absorbed by the film along path b than along path a, and from the number of electrons emerging at any point the film thickness at this point can be estimated. This number is given by the degree of blackening of a photographic plate placed in the path of the emerging electrons. On the other hand, the film thickness is, ideally, the depth of valleys on the original solid surface plus a constant, or a constant minus the height of hills. The validity of the assumptions on which this procedure is based should be tested in every instance, but usually the results of replica measurements are accepted without criticism.

Numerical Data on Surface Roughness

§7. EACH SURFACE has its own values of h_{av}, h_{max}, z^2, and so on, just as every object has its own mass. However, a range of probable roughness parameters can be given for each type of surface finish, especially on metals. Table II reproduces the typical values of h_{av} as found by a Committee of the American Society of Mechanical Engineers.[8]

TABLE II

AVERAGE HEIGHT OF HILLS PRODUCED BY VARIOUS TREATMENTS

	h_{av}	
	Microns	Microinches
Lapped or polished	0.02–0.25	1–10
Honed	0.10–0.50	4–20
Cold drawn or extruded	0.25–4	10–160
Die cast	0.40–4	16–160
Ground	0.50–2.5	20–100
Drilled	2.5 –5	100–200
Turned, shaped, milled, bored	3 –6	120–240

Stainless steel is usually sold in six "standard" finishes. Their h_{rms} may be expected to be 3–4 microns for finish No. 1, 0.3–1 micron for 2D (D is for dull), 0.1–0.4 micron for 2B (B is for bright), 0.04–0.05 for No. 4 in the direction of the grooves, 0.1 for No. 6 in the direction of the grooves, and 0.02–0.03 micron for No. 7 which has a mirror polish.

Surface roughness "comparators" consist of, for instance, 18 plates whose h_{rms} ranges from 0.05 to 12.5 microns; they are visually compared with surfaces under test.

Surface Porosity

§8. ALL SOLID SURFACES are rough and many are, in addition, porous.

A surface may be porous because the whole solid is porous; this is the case of wood, paper, textiles, leather, and so on. Or the porosity may be confined to a surface layer only, while the bulk of the solid is dense. Perhaps the best studied example of the second type is "anodized" aluminum.

Aluminum surfaces are anodically oxidized in a suitable electrolyte to produce relatively thick oxide films because such films impart an enhanced chemical and mechanical resistance to the material and also because they can be dyed. The film thickness may be less than one micron or exceed 10 microns;[9] at any rate it is of a microscopical rather than of a molecular dimension.

The porosity of the film can be determined, for instance, from its density;[10] if this is ρ and if ρ_0 is the density of perfect oxide crystals, the relative pore volume is $(\rho_0 - \rho)/\rho_0$, that is 1 cm.³ of the coating contains $(\rho_0 - \rho)/\rho_0$ cm.³ of air. The dimensions and the number of the pores can be found from electron micrographs of the films or their replicas.[11] The relative pore volume of coatings of industrial importance may be anything between 0.1 and 0.5, depending on the aluminum alloy treated and the treating procedure. The pore diameter often ranges between 0.01 and 0.05 micron, which means that the cross section of an average pore is near 4×10^{-12} cm.² If the relative pore volume is 0.2 and the pores extend through the whole depth of the film, then $0.2/4 \times 10^{-12} = 5 \times 10^{10}$ pores must be present on each cm.² of the surface.

The oxide layers, which form on metals in air and therefore are present on almost all metal surfaces kept under atmospheric conditions, are much thinner and much less porous than the films on "anodized" aluminum, but some porosity generally may be expected. When oxide crystals grow, the growth, as always, starts from discrete nuclei and gives rise to separate crystals; and it would not often happen that all these crystals would join each other without any interstices.

Metal coatings, such as of tin on blackplate (iron), also are porous, as a rule. The frequency of pores reaching almost to the iron surface is tested by chemical means in industrial laboratories and usually is quite small, but pores which do not traverse (almost) the whole thickness of the tin layer are not recorded in these tests and may be more numerous than those detected.

Glass, which was in contact with our humid atmosphere for any length of time, has a porous surface. Moisture condenses on the glass and leaches out the alkali present near the surface. Thus, a skeleton consisting chiefly of silica remains, and the space initially occupied by Na_2O, K_2O, and so on now is available to air. This process can be followed, for instance, by measuring the refractive index of the glass surface before and after exposure to air.

Variability along the Surface

§9. SEVERAL KINDS of this variability exist. If we follow any line along a surface, we shall meet a hill, then a valley, then another hill, and so forth; this is geometrical variability. Sometimes it is directed; e.g., the surface is covered with more or less distinct, more or less parallel grooves, and the variability across the grooves is greater than along these. Grooves produced by machining a metal can be seen at a small magnification, but much finer anisotropy can be detected by means of condensation phenomena. If a solid is rubbed with another and then breathed upon, water droplets may be preferentially oriented along the rubbing direction so that the "breath figure" obtained will reveal this direction. Or a dye solution is permitted to evaporate on the rubbed surface; the dye crystals thus formed may be oriented along the direction of the strokes in which case the surface will look differently along, and perpendicularly to, this direction. The natural anisotropy of wood surfaces and the difference between warp and weft in fabrics are too well known to be discussed in detail.

All metals used in daily life are polycrystalline, and the orientation of the crystals in space, as a rule, is approximately random.

Therefore, when a cut is made across a piece of metal, different crystals are cut under different angles to their crystallographic axes. Thus the area exposed differs in its crystallographic orientation from one to another spot. Since work function (that is, work required to remove an electron from the metal) depends on this orientation, electric properties of a metal surface vary from point to point. Apparently, also chemical reactivity depends on orientation and, consequently, is not identical for different surface regions.

Many common metals are alloys containing more than one phase, that is they contain two or more types of crystals, each type having a chemical composition different from that of the others. When a part made from such an alloy is cut, different phases are exposed in different regions of the surface. The electric potential difference between these phases is the main cause of corrosion of alloys. Its importance for the strength of adhints is mentioned in §98.

The variability caused by impurities should not be forgotten. The amount of finger grease transferred on a metal handle or a glass pane is sufficient for the detectives to reconstruct the fingerprint. It is also sufficient to affect the "breath figures" or many other thin deposits on the contaminated surface.

Variability across the Surface

§10. As a rule, chemical composition of a solid surface is different from that of the bulk, and the transition between the two compositions is gradual.

Metals have been extensively studied in this respect. Starting from the gas phase and proceeding toward the interior of a piece of metal, we meet first adsorbed gases and vapors, then dust and dirt partly embedded in (usually) an oil film, then a more or less porous layer of oxides, sulfides, and so on, then metal greatly distorted by the act of cutting (that is, by producing the surface), and finally metal having the bulk properties of the material.

The gas and vapor adsorption is touched upon in §§11 and 12. To make clear the importance of dust, it is sufficient to reproduce here some data[12] on the number of aerosol particles (i.e., of suspended grains and droplets) in 1 cm.^{3} of air, assuming 1 mg. being equivalent to 5×10^7 particles: in a dust storm or cloudburst 10^5 to 5×10^5; in a cotton mill up to 10^3; and in city air between 5 and 50.

The difficulty of removing the last traces of an oil which was once put on a solid is well illustrated in Table I, §5, which shows that an oil layer about as thick as h_{av} of the surface is not readily removed in the gravitational field.

Oxide layers on metal surfaces are mentioned, e.g., in §8. The oxide layer which gives the "natural" protection to aluminum in air (that is without any deliberate oxidation) is said to be about 10^{-7} cm. thick. The protective oxide coating on zinc may have a thickness of, for instance, 4×10^{-7} cm. Also the germanium oxide film on the surface of germanium transistors usually is from 10^{-7} to 5×10^{-7} cm. thick, and the whole action of transistors depends on this film.

The existence of modified metal near the surface is proved, for instance, by metallographic examination of sections perpendicular to the original surface. Another method is based on the measurement of "microhardness," that is of the stress required to produce a small, definite indentation in the surface. It is found that this stress varies when the depth of indentation increases; consequently, true hardness of the material must vary with the distance from the surface. Usually, surface layers, because of machining and similar treatments, are harder than the underlying metal. Figure 8 is an example of this behavior.[13] The abscissa of the graph represents the force on the indenter; when this force increases, the depth of indentation also increases. The ordinate is the stress needed for a definite indentation. The ordinates are smaller at greater forces; this means that microhardness is smaller at greater depths. The upper curve refers to a mechanically polished single crystal of aluminum and the lower curve to the same crystal after electropolishing. Electropolishing removes the distorted external layers; therefore, the variation of

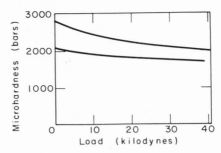

FIG. 8. Dependence of hardness on depth. Abscissa: load in kilodynes. Ordinate: stress (in bars) needed for a standard indentation. Upper curve: mechanically polished aluminum. Lower curve: electropolished aluminum. Data of reference 13.

microhardness with depth is less pronounced for the lower than for the upper curve.

The removal of the distorted material by electropolishing often is chemically selective; if the metal, as usual, contains various ingredients, their rate of dissolution will not be identical, the surface will lose more of the active than of the less active component, and, after treatment, will contain a higher relative amount of the latter.

Surface layers produced by corrosion of glass are mentioned in §8. Their existence is well shown by measurements of surface conductance. When a glass cylinder is placed between two metal electrodes and alternating current is sent from one to the other metal disc, the major part of the current proceeds in the thin layer along the surface of the glass. The thickness of this film can be estimated from optical measurements, §8; let it be δ cm. The measured resistance Ω of the cylinder, from Ohm's law, is $\Omega = l/2\pi r\delta\kappa$, l being the distance between the electrodes, r the radius of the cylinder, and κ the conductivity of the material of the surface film. This κ was on quartz nearly equal to that of a saturated solution of quartz in water, and on glass it was equal to the conductivity of a dilute sodium hydroxide solution. The thickness δ was, for instance, 5×10^{-7} cm.[14]

Surface conductance is valuable also for studying semiconductor surfaces. If, for instance, a material conducts electricity because it contains an excess of electrons, and gas molecules which readily accept electrons are adsorbed on its surface, then adsorbed particles become negative ions and these ions electrostatically repel free electrons in the lattice with the result that there is a deficiency of electrons immediately adjacent to the adsorbed layer and a corresponding change in surface conductivity.[15]

In §4 a method for estimating the surface area of a solid was mentioned, based on the observation that the most exterior atoms (or ions) react with the surrounding more rapidly than those less accessible. More elaborate measurements demonstrate that the isotope exchange between a gas and a solid alters its rate rather gradually when the depth of the solid affected increases. Thus,[16] when gaseous chlorine was admitted to a vessel containing sodium chloride crystals tagged with Cl^{36}, the transfer of radioactivity into the gas phase continued, albeit at a low rate, also when all the surface ions must have been exchanged.

Gas Adsorption

§11.   ADSORPTION of foreign atoms and molecules by solids is important for understanding adhesion because, when adhints are made, an intimate contact between two different kinds of atoms (of the adherend and the adhesive) is desired, and one of the two components is solid, while adsorption is the best studied facet of just this phenomenon of making contact between a solid and another substance. Since adhesives are applied as liquids rather than as gases, adsorption of liquids would be a more fitting effect to consider, but gas adsorption is fundamentally similar to that of liquids and is easier to comprehend. It is briefly surveyed in this and the following section, while §13 deals with the interaction between liquids and solid surfaces.

When a gas is admitted in an evacuated space containing a solid or liquid body M, or when a gas stream is forced through a powder or a liquid, a part of the gas is seen to "disappear." Experimentally this means that, when so much gas is introduced that its final pressure should be p_0, the actual pressure is p_1 and $p_1 < p_0$; analogously, if v_0 cm.³ of gas was present before bubbling, only v_1 cm.³ is recovered after it, and $v_1 < v_0$. In the instance of a liquid we say that $v_0 - v_1$ cm.³ was absorbed in, or dissolved by, the liquid. In the instance of a solid we say that volume $v_0 - v_1$ was adsorbed.

For a time, the mechanisms of absorption and adsorption were believed to be entirely different. At present, it seems best to consider both phenomena from one point of view. A uniform condensed body M of mass m would, in equilibrium, dissolve, say, x g. of gas at the (final) pressure p_1. The equilibrium is relatively easily attained as long as M is a liquid of moderate viscosity. In this instance, convection and diffusion in a reasonable time would distribute the gas molecules, which of course enter first the surface layer, over the whole volume of the liquid. However, there is no convection in a solid and the rate of diffusion usually is only a small fraction of that in a liquid. Consequently the gas, in the short time allowed for laboratory experiments, cannot penetrate far from the surface, and only that fraction of the solid volume takes part in dissolving the gas which, as mentioned in §§8 and 10, is porous or distorted.

A typical gas adsorption experiment starts with degassing the solid (i.e., the *adsorbent*) at a high temperature; then the adsorbent is permitted to cool to the chosen temperature, and gas is brought in contact with it. The pretreatment is necessary if adsorption uncomplicated by desorption is the object of study. An unheated adsorbent contains gases and vapors originating from its previous environment; thus a solid previously kept in air has moisture, oxygen, and other constituents of the atmosphere present in its surface layer. When such a solid is introduced in a vessel filled with, say, krypton, this gas has to displace some adsorbed molecules of H_2O, O_2, etc., before it can be adsorbed; thus, adsorption of Kr depends on desorption of other gases.

Solid adherends are not heated and degassed before the application of an adhesive, but the fact that adsorbents are, is instructive; it demonstrates the tenacity with which adsorbed atoms and molecules cling to the solid phase. When an adhesive is applied, it must cause desorption of pre-adsorbed compounds from the surface; this step is discussed in §16.

§12.   WHEN IT IS ASKED, which of the two gases G_1 and G_2 is likely to be adsorbed by M in a greater amount, the answer depends on both chemical and physical factors. If G_1 can, and G_2 cannot, chemically react with M, then adsorption of G_1 is likely to be the greater one; thus oxygen is more avidly taken up by active carbons than nitrogen is. If neither of the gases has a "chemical affinity" to M, then either the reduced temperature T/T_c or the relative pressure p_1/p_s is deciding. As in §11, p_1 is the gas pressure around the adsorbent at equilibrium, T is the absolute temperature of the experiment, T_c the absolute critical temperature of the gas, and p_s is saturation pressure at temperature T. Ratio T/T_c is more useful when T is greater than T_c, and p_1/p_s is more useful when $T < T_c$. The amount adsorbed usually is greater when T/T_c is smaller and p_1/p_s is greater. For instance, at atmospheric pressure at 35°, the adsorbed amount x/m of carbon dioxide as a rule will be found to exceed that of methane because the critical temperatures for these substances are 304.2 and 191.0°K. thus making the ratio T/T_c equal to 1.01 and 1.61, respectively. At 20°C., x/m of carbon dioxide generally will be smaller than that of n-butane (both at atmospheric pressure) because in these conditions p_1/p_s is approximately 0.49 for butane and 0.018 for CO_2.

All ingredients of customary adhesives are far below their critical points during application and their saturation pressures p_s at the application temperature generally are very small; thus, as long as no chemical reaction intervenes, adhesives may be expected to be adsorbed preferentially to the main ingredients of our atmosphere (nitrogen, oxygen, noble gases, carbon dioxide, and, less safely, water).

The behavior outlined in the two preceding paragraphs is altered when wetting effects interfere. At small values of p_1/p_s, for instance less than 0.3, the adsorbed amount is greater when the vapor belongs to a liquid which wets the adsorbent. This is readily noticed when the relative adsorbed amount, that is amount x taken up at a small p_1/p_s divided by the amount x_s adsorbed at p_s, rather than x itself, is considered. If x/x_s is plotted as a function of p_1/p_s, the curve for a substance which wets the adsorbent usually lies higher than the curve for a poorly wetting compound. This is true, for instance, for the adsorption of benzene (well wetting) and water (poorly wetting) by commercial active carbons. The importance of wetting in the application of adhesives is discussed in §§16 to 23.

At large values of p_1/p_s, say at $p_1/p_s > 0.9$, the amount adsorbed is approximately determined by the rule that the *liquid volume* taken up is independent of the liquid. An illustration of this rule is presented in Fig. 9 based on one of the earliest

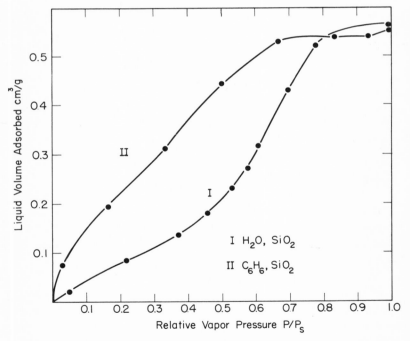

Fig. 9. Adsorption isotherms of water vapor (lower curve) and benzene vapor (upper curve) on dry silica gel at 15°. Abscissa: relative vapor pressure. Ordinate: liquid volume adsorbed by 1 g. gel, in cm.³. Data of reference 17.

confirmations of this rule.[17] Its abscissa is p_1/p_s at 15°, and its
ordinate shows the liquid volumes (that is mass x divided by
the density of the liquid at 15°) adsorbed by 1 g. of solid silica
gel; the volumes are expressed in cm.[3]. It is seen that the adsorbed volumes are different for benzene and water as long as
p_1/p_s is less than 0.8 but are almost identical at $p_1/p_s > 0.8$.
The explanation for this behavior is that at high relative vapor
pressures the pores of the adsorbent are filled with the liquid,
and the volume taken up is simply the volume of the pores.
Thus, one gram of the silica gel studied by Anderson contained
0.56 cm.[3] of pores. It was mentioned in §1 that one of the main
tasks to be accomplished by an adhesive is to fill the valleys on
the surface of the adherend; Fig. 9 teaches us that this state can
be reached even if the filling substance is a vapor.

At small values of p_1/p_s, the quantity adsorbed often is proportional to the area of the adsorbent, and this area can be calculated from the adsorption isotherm. Adsorption isotherms are
curves of x/m versus p_1/p_s, as in Fig. 9, or versus p_1. For instance, if N_1 is the number of nitrogen molecules taken up by one
gram of a solid at -195.8°C. and 63 millibars ($=47$ mm. Hg)
or at -183.0° and 323 millibars, then the surface area of this
gram (i.e., the specific surface area of the solid) is 15 N_1 square
angstroms.

Adsorption from Solutions

§13.   THE MAJORITY of industrial adhesives in the moment
of application are solutions, and adsorption undoubtedly occurs when these solutions are brought in contact with solid surfaces.

When an adsorbent is introduced in a solution containing
y_0 g. solute for each $1 - y_0$ grams of solvent, the concentration
of the liquid changes and its final composition may be expressed
as y grams of solute for each $1 - y$ grams of solvent. Thus, apparently, $y_0 - y$ grams of solute was adsorbed from each gram
of solution. This, however, is only an apparent adsorption because it is not known how much of the solvent was taken up

when the solute was adsorbed. To make the relation clearer, let us denote the true adsorbed amounts, from 1 g. of solution, z_1 and z_2 for solute and solvent, respectively. Then, $1 - z_1 - z_2$ g. of liquid remains, and $y = (y_0 - z_1)/(1 - z_1 - z_2)$. Solving for z_1 we obtain

$$z_1 = \frac{y_0 - y + yz_2}{1 - y}.$$

As long as z_2 is unknown, no value can be given for z_1. Only if there is a reason to believe that z_2 is negligible and if $y \ll 1$, it is permitted to set $z_1 = y_0 - y$.

Experimentally, the apparent adsorption $(y_0 - y)/m$ from dilute solutions is approximately as large as the vapor adsorption x/m at large p_1/p_s values, if the solute has a much higher critical temperature, or a much higher melting point, or a much greater molecular weight than the solvent has. It is natural to believe that in these instances $z_2 \ll z_1$ and the apparent adsorption is nearly equal to the true one. Thus, if the adhesive contains a polymer mixed with low-molecular liquids, we may expect the polymer to be adsorbed preferentially to the other components. However, chemical effects, see §12, may upset this rule.

The surface area of the adsorbent can be calculated from z_1 in a manner analogous to that outlined in §12.

Additional information on the topics covered in §§2 to 13 can be found, for instance, in reference 18.

REFERENCES

1. Bikerman, J. J., *Chem. Age (London)* **47**, 186 (1942).
2. Bikerman, J. J., *J. Colloid Sci.* **11**, 299 (1956).
3. Bikerman, J. J., *J. Colloid Sci.* **5**, 349 (1950).
4. Hull, H. H., *Proc. 8th Tech. Meeting Tech. Assoc. Graphic Arts 1956* A, p. 53 (1956).
5. Tolansky, S., Multiple-Beam Interferometry of Surfaces and Films. Clarendon Press, Oxford, 1948.
6. Sugg, R. E., *Chem. Eng.* **61**, No. 3, 216 (1954).
7. Blet, G., *Publs. sci. et tech. ministère air (France) No.* **241** (1950).
8. American Standards Assoc. B 46.1. Am. Soc. Mech. Engineers, New York, 1955.

9. Spooner, R. C., *J. Electrochem. Soc.* **102**, 156 (1955).

10. Mason, R. B., *Metal Finishing* **55**, No. 8, 55 (1957).

11. Keller, F., Hunter, M. S., and Robinson, D. L., *J. Electrochem. Soc.* **100**, 411 (1953).

12. Drinker, P., and Hatch, T., "Industrial Dust," 2nd ed., p. 99. McGraw-Hill, New York, 1954.

13. Popilov, L. Ya., and Zaitseva, L. P., "Electropolishing and Electroetching of Metallographic Sections," p. 63. GNTI Literature Iron and Noniron Metallurgy, Moscow, 1955.

14. Kuznetsov, A. Ya., *Zhur. Fiz. Khim.* **27**, 657 (1953).

15. Statz, H., et al., *in* "Semiconductor Surface Physics" (R. H. Kingston, ed.), p. 139, Univ. of Penn. Press, Philadelphia, 1957.

16. Harrison, L. G., Morrison, J. A., and Rose, G. S., *in* "Surface Activity" (J. H. Schulman, ed.), Vol. 2, p. 287. Academic Press, New York, 1957.

17. Anderson, J. S., *Z. physik. Chem.* **88**, 191 (1914).

18. Bikerman, J. J., "Surface Chemistry," 2nd ed. Academic Press, New York, 1958.

CHAPTER 2

Adhesive and Other Joints

§14. Two SOLIDS can be fastened together without an adhesive. Probably no one misunderstands the action of a rivet. A nail driven into wood is fastened to the latter not by any molecular adhesion but by the pressure exerted by the wood on the nail; the nail pushes the wood around it away thus causing compression of the wood, and the compressed wood in its turn presses on the nail. Obviously, no removal of weak boundary layers, §1, is needed for this type of joining.

While the attachment of a nail to a board is as well understood as the action of a rivet, misunderstanding sometimes occurs when there are many nail-like protuberances on the surface and these are too small to be visible to the unaided eye, see §3; in such instances, the protuberances may be overlooked and the fastening effect confused with adhesion. Thus, when a hard metal is pressed into a soft metal (such as indium), an effort is required to raise the "plunger" again.

A markedly greater effort is needed to separate two solids if they were not only pressed together but also wrung together or suffered another mutual tangential displacement. The degree of joining achieved in this operation may be illustrated by the following examples. When two optically flat glass surfaces were worked into a "contact" at which the average clearance between them was about 1.5×10^{-5} cm., a force of nearly 10^5 dynes per cm.^{2} was required to shear the joint.[1] When two metal bars were similarly wrung together under a pressure of, for instance, 10^8 dynes/cm.^{2}, an approximately equal tensile stress was needed to break them apart.[2] A gold wire squashed and spread over the quartz surface can be used as a suspension for a quartz crystal. The ancient art of gilding copper and other metals by mechanical means at temperatures far below the melting point of gold also should be mentioned here.

The mechanism of this effect apparently has never been investigated. The following explanations are advanced as the most probable guesses in the present state of our knowledge.

If the separation is achieved by a movement normal to the plane of contact, it can be compared to the extraction of a snap fastener or a nail. If, for instance, an eminence (A) is forced into depression (B) on the opposite surface, see Fig. 10, the walls of

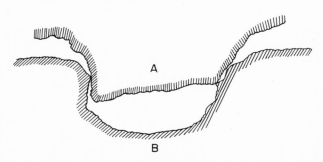

FIG. 10. Mechanical attachment of the snap-fastener type.

B are elastically pushed apart and then exert a lateral pressure on A; this is the mechanism of a snap fastener. If no preformed depression is present, A can act as a nail. The function of wringing is to increase the probability of these processes. If the two solids are pressed together without any tangential motion, an eminence which may have a diameter of about 1 micron and, consequently, an area of about 10^{-8} cm.^{2}, will be in contact with only 10^{-8} cm.^{2} of the other surface, and on this minute area the surface of B may offer no suitable indentation for a snap and no weak spot for a nail. If the tangential motion was such that each protuberance traveled 1 cm., it was in contact with 10^{-4} cm.^{2} of the surface of B; hence, the probability of meeting a suitable contour was much greater. In some instances, the interpenetration of A and B is such that we may speak of "plastic mixing"; mixing which took place on wringing together a copper and an aluminum rod can be seen in the microphotographs of reference 3.

If separation is achieved by a shearing motion, the force needed for it presumably is analogous to the force needed to spread butter over bread or to maintain uniform sliding of a drop along an inclined plane, see §§5 and 23. When a liquid drop (or a chunk of butter) moves along a solid surface, those parts of it above the surface hills can—in favorable circumstances— maintain a steady motion parallel to the surface; but those parts of the liquid which must meander between the hills cannot keep pace with the higher layers and remain behind as a wet track left by the drop. As long as viscosity (or consistency) is small, the tension $F_n \sin \alpha/w$ of §5 is determined by the surface tension of the liquid in the wake of the drop; when the drop slides along dx cm., the liquid-air interface behind it increases by $kw \cdot dx$ cm.^{2}, k being the ratio of the combined widths of the wet tracks to the width of the drop.

An interpenetration almost as pronounced as in "plastic mixing" is illustrated in Fig. 11. It is a 530-fold enlargement of

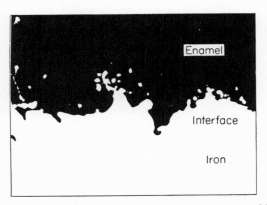

Fig. 11. Interface of sandblasted iron and porcelain enamel. Magnification 530×. From reference 4.

a section of the interface between sandblasted iron and porcelain enamel;[4] enamel dendrites penetrating into iron and iron filaments embedded in enamel are clearly visible in the photograph. Adherence of enamel to iron seems to be greater the more numerous these dendrites and filaments, but apparently it is not known whether this mechanical interlocking is the only or at least the main cause of adherence.

An even higher degree of interpenetration is achieved in hooking and weaving which, of course, are understood by everyone. The strength of many adhesive joints is based on an analogous mechanism. For these adhints, as for nails, removal of weak boundary layers is superfluous. They are obtained with fibrous materials such as paper, cardboard, or fabrics; the liquid adhesive penetrates into the pores of the adherend and eventually solidifies around the filaments of the latter. It is clear that, as soon as the structure indicated in Fig. 12 is attained, i.e., the

Fig. 12. Penetration of adhesive in a fibrous material.

adhesive completely or to a considerable extent surrounds a fiber, the two materials cannot be separated without tearing at least one of them. In these instances, the adhesive acts simply as a hook. This has been understood for many years, see, for instance, reference 5, and apparently can be seen at the adhesive: paper ratio as small as 4:100.[6] The strength due to interpenetration naturally is almost independent of the surface treatment of the fabric; this was demonstrated, for instance, by nitration and acetylation of cotton.[7]

True Adhesive Joints

§15.   In true adhesive joints, that is those that do not rely on the interpenetration of the hook type, five layers can be recognized. They are: first adherend–first boundary layer–adhesive film–second boundary layer–second adherend. If the two adherends are identical, their boundary layers also are likely to be identical (see, however, §§24 and 42) and there are only three different strata, namely the two adherends, the two boundary layers, and the adhesive film (also known as *glue line*). In exceptional instances, boundary layers are absent, but the adhints of this kind belong, for instance, to high-vacuum physics rather than to any industry utilizing adhesives.

When an adhint is broken by mechanical means, rupture can occur in the adherends, or in the adhesive, or in one of the boundary layers. When the adherend gives way first, the science of adhesive joints is not involved. If the adhesive breaks, the joints are termed *proper*,[8] and they are *improper* if rupture proceeds along a boundary layer.

It is interesting to note that proper adhints usually are not broken at all. If, for instance, a leather strip is glued to a shoe heel, the strip and the heel are never separated; the whole shoe is discarded and destroyed when it ceases to be usable. An identical observation applies to the combinations postal stamp–adhesive–envelope, couch leg–adhesive–couch, and so on. On the other hand, improper joints often fail when the rest of the assembly is still perfectly sound. Thus, control and research laboratories have to deal with them. Customers, fortunately, deal mainly with proper joints.

The history of an adhint usually comprises three periods. During the first the adhesive is applied, during the second it sets, and during the third its properties remain constant or almost constant; Chapters III and IV treat the first stage, Chapter V is concerned with the second, and Chapters VI to IX deal with the third. The necessity of three stages follows from the discussion, §1, of the function of an adhesive. It must be applied liquid to displace weak boundary layers and to fill the depressions; this is period No. 1. The majority of the adhesives are expected to be strong and, consequently, must be solid all their "working life"; this is period No. 3. Period No. 2 is the transition from No. 1 to No. 3.

The so-called *pressure-sensitive* adhesives (for which also a better name, namely *permanently tacky* is used) set so slowly that the third period is not observed in their use. Adhesive tapes, insulating tapes, and similar goods contain such adhesives. The mechanism of their action is outlined in Chapter IV.

In systematizing the research on adhints, the square shown as Fig. 13 often is helpful. It emphasizes the existence of 9

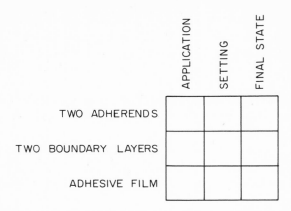

FIG. 13. Nine fields of study in the science of adhesive joints.

distinct fields of study and facilitates placing any piece of information in its proper position relative to other available information.

REFERENCES

1. Macaulay, J. M., *Nature* **138,** 587 (1936).
2. Anderson, O. L., *J. Appl. Phys.* **30,** 593 (1959).
3. Anderson, O. L., *Bell Labs. Record* **35,** 441 (1957).
4. Richmond, J. C., Moore, D. G., Kirkpatrick, H. R., and Harrison, W. N., *Natl. Advisory Comm. Aeronaut. Rept.* **1166.**
5. Clark, G. L., *Colloid Symposium Monograph* **4,** 145 (1926).
6. Bursztyn, I. *Brit. Plastics* **20,** 299 (1948).
7. Borroff, E. M., and Wake, W. C., *Trans. Inst. Rubber Ind.* **25,** 191 (1949).
8. Bikerman, J. J., *in* "Rheology" (F. R. Eirich, ed.), Vol. 3, p. 479. Academic Press, New York, 1960.

CHAPTER 3

Formation of Adhesive Joints

Wetting

§16. To DISPLACE AIR from the surface of a solid, the adhesive must wet the latter. The degree of wetting is quantitatively expressed in terms of contact angle. Contact angle is the angle (in the liquid) between the air-liquid and the liquid-solid interface. In Fig. 14, showing a drop on a horizontal plane, it is acute, and in Fig. 15, showing a meniscus in a capillary, it is obtuse. Letter θ generally is used to denote contact angle. If the solid is flat, that is encloses an angle of 180°, the angle occupied by the gas space is $180 - \theta°$.

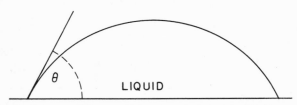

LIQUID

FIG. 14. A drop on a horizontal plane. θ is the contact angle.

The value of θ, as would be expected, depends on the composition of the three phases in contact but is affected also by surface roughness, §3, and by the pre-history of the system. Because of these complications it is impossible to assign a definite value to the contact angle when the chemical nature of the solid, the liquid and the gas is known. In this respect contact angles unfortunately differ from any other properties of 3-phase systems, such as vapor pressure of a solution in equilibrium with the excess solid. In §17 and §18 the methods are indicated which serve to delineate the region of values in which the equilibrium contact angle for any chemically defined system must be situated, that is the angle which would be observed on a perfectly smooth solid surface in the absence of any time effects (of which hysteresis of wetting, §20, is the most important).

For these equilibrium contact angles only two general, qualitative rules are known. Provided the gas is our common air,

(a) the θ is smaller the smaller the surface tension γ of the liquid, as long as the solid is not modified by the contact with the latter; and

(b) when the solid swells in, or otherwise mixes with, the liquid, θ is smaller than would be expected from the value of γ.

To (a): In 1806 Laplace formulated the hypothesis that $\gamma(1 + \cos \theta)$ was a constant characteristic for each solid (in air) and independent of the liquid. As a crude approximation, this relation seems to be correct. This is illustrated by Table III (unpublished data).

TABLE III

EQUILIBRIUM CONTACT ANGLES BETWEEN AIR, SOLIDS, AND LIQUIDS AT 21° AND 50% RELATIVE HUMIDITY

Liquid	Its γ g.sec.$^{-2}$	$\gamma(1 + \cos \theta)$	
		Polyethylene	Aluminum
Water	73	62	108
Glycerol	64	59	93
Benzyl benzoate	43	83	86

A more extensive material exists[1] for "maximum advancing contact angles," see §20, which are several degrees larger than the equilibrium angles. The product $\gamma(1 + \cos \theta_A)$ was, in air at 20° and 50% relative humidity, on a copolymer of tetrafluoroethylene and chlorotrifluoroethylene, 60 for water, 49 for tetradecane, a dioctyl phthalate, and benzene, 48 for a dioctyl ether, 46 for dodecane and a diamyl ether, and so on.

To (b): The expression $\gamma(1 + \cos \theta)$, if it is constant at all, obviously can be constant only as long as the solid remains constant, that is, is not altered by the contact with the liquid. The increase of this product (and the corresponding decrease of angle θ) caused by miscibility of liquid and solid is particularly striking in the instance of mercury. The γ of mercury in air is

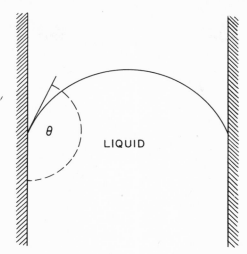

FIG. 15. Meniscus in a capillary. θ is the contact angle.

approximately 450 g.sec.$^{-2}$ and θ at the air–mercury–glass boundary usually is near 130°, so that $\gamma(1 + \cos \theta) \approx 161$. For nonreactive liquids, the product $\gamma(1 + \cos \theta)$ for copper is not very different from this for glass, but copper forms an amalgam with mercury and the amalgam is perfectly wetted by the latter, meaning that $\theta = 0$; hence $\gamma(1 + \cos \theta)$ for air, mercury, and copper is near 900 g.sec.$^{-2}$.

Analogous effects are quite common. Suppose that a polymer is not attacked by liquid A but swells in liquid B, surface tension being identical for the two liquids; contact angle θ will be smaller for the air–B–polymer than for the air–A–polymer system.

The effect of the composition of the gas phase on θ is large but presumably is more often indirect than direct; gas composition affects θ because it alters the composition of the solid-gas interface. Consider, for instance, water vapor in air. This vapor is readily adsorbed by all common solid surfaces, as follows from §12; there exists no other important component of the atmosphere whose p_1/p_s is as high as the p_1/p_s of water. When relative humidity changes between 0% and 100%, the composition of the solid surface changes between 100% solid and almost

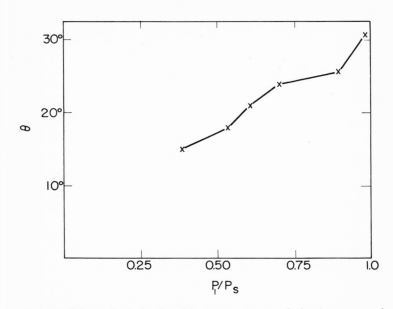

Fig. 16. Effect of relative humidity on contact angle in the system air, acetylene tetrabromide, and quartz. Abscissa: relative humidity. Ordinate: contact angle. Date of reference 2.

100% water. It is clear that contact angle should change accordingly. Figure 16, based on the data of Bartell and Bristol,[2] illustrates this change. Its abscissa is the relative humidity of air, and its ordinate, the contact angle (probably not very different from the equilibrium contact angle) at the air–sym. tetrabromoethane–quartz boundary.

Although this ought to be clear from the foregoing discussion, it may be emphasized here that the value of the contact angle is not a reliable measure of molecular attraction between the solid and the liquid; this point seems to be sometimes overlooked. Contact angle depends on all 3 phases in contact and can give information only on the *relative* strength of the attractions between solid and liquid on one hand and solid and gas on the other hand; the greater the first attraction compared with the second, the smaller the contact angle (in the liquid!). However, the solid–liquid attraction can still be very strong even if the contact angle is large.

Measurement of Contact Angles

§17. THERE are four main methods of measuring contact angles.

1. A sessile drop, such as illustrated in Fig. 14, is observed directly, or photographed, or its image is projected on a screen. For direct observation, a low-power microscope whose eyepiece is provided with a filament is conveneint. First the filament is set so as to coincide with the visible base line of the drop, and then it is turned to lie along the tangent to the drop at its base. The angle through which the filament must be rotated is the contact angle. On a photograph or a projected image contact angle is measured, *e.g.*, with a protractor.

The method is very simple and easy but does not give exact results because the tangent rapidly changes along the vertical cross section of the drop and it is difficult to make sure that the tangent measured indeed belongs to the lowest point of this cross section. The change of tangent at a point with the height of this point is not easily calculated for a round drop but can be expressed by a simple equation if the meniscus along a flat vertical wall is observed. In this instance,

$$\cos \theta = \frac{g\rho h^2}{2\gamma}$$

g being acceleration due to gravity, ρ density of liquid minus density of air, h the vertical distance between the horizontal expanse of the liquid surface and the 3-phase line (in which gas, liquid, and solid meet), and γ is surface tension. For water in air at room temperature, γ is approximately 72 g.sec.$^{-2}$ and $g\rho/2\gamma$ is about 6.8 cm.$^{-2}$. Thus, for example, for $\cos \theta = 0.68$, $h = 0.316$ cm. If the tangent is observed 0.05 cm. above the true 3-phase line, see Fig. 17, then $h = 0.266$ cm., $h^2 = 0.0708$ cm.^{2}, and $\cos \theta = 0.481$. It is usually believed that angle θ measured by this method is correct within $\pm 1°$ or $\pm 2°$.

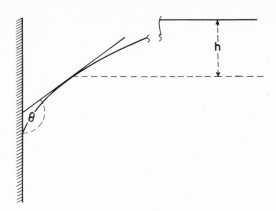

FIG. 17. Meniscus along a vertical wall.

2. The method of level surface is a little less simple and has a higher precision; it requires a large volume of liquid and thus is better suitable for water than for less common substances. Its principle is shown in Fig. 18. Plate 1 is partly immersed in the liquid (2). It is rotated about the horizontal axis 3 until the liquid surface is flat all the way to the solid plate. Angle θ is then read on the protractor scale 4. As a rule, visual inspection is sufficient to determine whether the liquid is or is not flat at

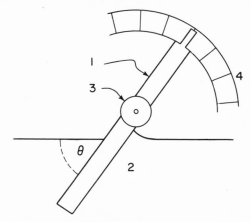

FIG. 18. The level-surface method of measuring contact angle.

the 3-phase line; if necessary, a narrow beam of light is directed on this line and the presence of any curved meniscus is detected from the shape of the reflected beam.

A horizontal cylinder can be used instead of a tilted plate, especially when the contact angle is less or not much greater than 90°. Figure 19 represents a vertical view of the setup. The

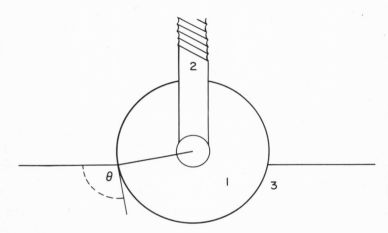

Fig. 19. The lying-cylinder method of measuring contact angle.

cylinder (1) can be raised or lowered with a screw (2), and its height is adjusted so that the liquid (3) is flat right to the solid surface. The angle can be calculated, for instance, from the displacement of the screw. If the area of the liquid surface is much greater than πr^2, r being the radius of the cylinder, then the distance l, by which the screw is moved from the point at which the cylinder just touches the liquid to the position in which the surface is level, is $l = r(1 + \cos \theta)$.

§18. 3. CONTACT ANGLE θ can be calculated from the dimensions of a sessile drop. The computation would be quite simple if the drops were parts of a sphere. For part-spherical drops, the height would be equal to $r(1 - \cos \theta)$, the volume equal to $(\pi/3)r^3(1 - \cos \theta)^2(2 + \cos \theta)$, and the diameter of the base $2r \cdot \sin \theta$. Thus, any two of these quantities would be sufficient to calculate both angle θ and r, i.e., the radius of the sphere whose segment the droplet is. As determination of the height is not easy because the bottom of the drop may be obscured by the waviness of the solid surface, see §17, it is easier to use volume v and base diameter Δ. The ratio

$$\frac{\Delta^3}{v} = \frac{24 \sin^3\theta}{\pi(2 - 3 \cos \theta + \cos^3\theta)} \tag{1}$$

and a table for computing θ from the experimental values of Δ^3/v is available.[3]

The drops, however, are not segments of a sphere as they are distorted by gravitation. Tables accounting for this distortion exist (see, for instance, reference 4) but sometimes it is easier to measure Δ^3/v for several drops of different volumes and to extrapolate the ratio to $v = 0$. The extrapolated ratio satisfies equation (1).

The main source of error in this determination is revealing. It is generally found that diameter Δ is not constant along the circumference of the drop, however carefully the drop has been deposited; different diameters of the base may easily differ from each other by several per cents. The mean value of all measured diameters is set in equation (1) to calculate θ but the calculated angle obviously also is an average; as solid surfaces are not uniform, the real contact angle along, say, one micron of the 3-phase boundary is a little different from that along the next micron.

4. The method of capillary pull often is convenient. A thin solid plate is vertically suspended at one end of a balance beam or on a calibrated spring. Let the weight of the plate in air be W_0. When a dish containing liquid is placed under the plate so that the lower edge of the latter is immersed, a weight W_1 will be found necessary to counterbalance the force on the plate. This force is a sum of three components:

$$W_1 = W_0 - B + L\gamma \cos \theta.$$

The buoyancy B decreases the apparent weight of the plate and the capillary force (equal to the weight of the liquid meniscus lifted or depressed at the solid) $L\gamma \cos \theta$ augments it when θ is

< 90° and diminishes it when θ is > 90°. L is the perimeter of the horizontal cross section of the plate.

The buoyancy term B is not easy to determine with precision. It is $B = abh\,\rho\,g$, if a is the width, b the thickness of the plate, h the depth of its immersion in the liquid, g acceleration due to gravity, and ρ density of the liquid minus density of air. The value of h is the quantity which eludes a simple measurement. To make the error in W_1, caused by the inexact knowledge of B, as small as possible, the plate immersion h is made small and the plate is selected as thin as feasible. It is clear that ratio of B to $L\gamma\,\cos\,\theta$ is proportional to ab/L, that is to $ab/2(a + b)$ and thus tends to zero when b tends to zero. When a foil 0.0025 cm. (= 0.001 inch) thick is used in a 10-cm. width, γ is 72 g.sec.$^{-2}$ (as for water), $\cos\,\theta = 0.5$ and $h = 0.05$ cm., then $B = 1.25$ g.cm./sec.^{2} and $\gamma L \cdot \cos\,\theta = 720$ g.cm./sec.^{2}. Thus, even a considerable error in B will not markedly affect the calculated value of $\cos\,\theta$ in this instance.

§19.   THE GREAT SENSITIVITY of contact angles to the cleanness of the solid has already been referred to (§16). To emphasize the warning, it may be mentioned that deposition of 5×10^{-8} g. of a triphenylmethane dye ("Night Blue") on 1 cm.^{2} of glass raised θ at the air–water–glass boundary from 0° to 35°[5] and deposition of 0.00015 mg. of octylamine on 1 cm.^{2} of platinum made the platinum surface identical with octylamine surface as far as wetting was concerned.[6]

As stated in §16, contact angle on a given solid often is smaller the smaller the surface tension γ of the liquid. But γ is very easily lowered (not raised) by impurities. Hence, if liquid in a particular test contains traces of surface-active materials, it may wet the solid adherend while, in a duplicate test, only imperfect wetting may be realized because the liquid was more thoroughly purified.

If the chemical compositions of solid and liquid are identical in the two tests, the duplicate experiment still may give a different result as long as surface roughness of the adherend is not kept constant. The effect of rugosity on contact angle is easily understood when it is realized that each groove on the surface acts similarly to a capillary tube in which liquid rises above or descends below the main level of the liquid outside. If the real equilibrium angle is $> 90°$, the liquid in the groove will contract, and at $\theta < 90°$ it will spread, compared to a drop on an absolutely smooth solid. The effect of this unequal spreading is particularly transparent in the methods of §18. When θ is $< 90°$, the measured Δ is greater, and at $\theta > 90°$ Δ is smaller than on a smooth surface. As equation (1) is valid for a drop on a plane, θ calculated from it would be too small in the first and too great in the second instance. Thus, even if rugosity has no effect on the real θ (that is θ on submicroscopical scale), it renders the calculated angles smaller when they are small and greater when they are great. The effect of roughness on the weight of meniscus, in method No. 4, is of the same kind. The amount of liquid hanging on a rough vertical slide is greater or smaller than on a smooth slide according to whether θ is smaller of greater than 90°; thus rugosity again exaggerates the difference between acute and obtuse contact angles.

Hysteresis of Wetting

§20.   Some difficulties encountered when measuring contact angles were outlined in the preceding sections but hysteresis of wetting is probably an even greater obstacle to obtaining reliable values for θ. This hysteresis is observed in all 4 procedures described in §§17 and 18. If a drop is placed on a horizontal plate, contact angle is determined either directly or from the drop dimensions, and then a small droplet is added to the initial drop, it is found that the 3-phase line does not shift, that is the drop becomes taller and contact angle greater; see a and b in Fig. 20.[7]

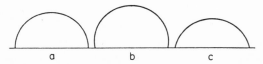

Fig. 20. Hysteresis of wetting. The base of the drop does not change when volume increases from a to b or decreases from a to c.

When more liquid is added, the drop continues to increase in volume but not in the area of the base until the contact angle reaches a more or less definite value called "the maximum advancing contact angle"; then the drop spreads with a jerk and the new contact angle is similar to that of the initial drop. If, instead of adding liquid to the drop, liquid is gradually removed from it, drop *a* gets flatter, see drop *c*, until "the minimum receding contact angle" is reached, when the drop suddenly contracts.

In the level surface method, contact angle is smaller when the slide, in rotating, emerges from the liquid, and greater when the liquid invades the slide surface.

In the fourth method, capillary pull initially is greater the further the vertical foil is lifted, see Fig. 21 in which the con-

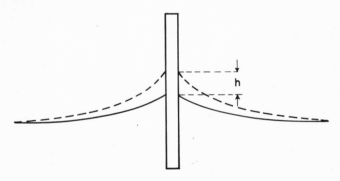

Fɪɢ. 21. The capillary-pull method of measuring hysteresis of wetting.

tinuous line represents the meniscus before, and the dotted line the meniscus after, the foil was lifted by distance *h*. When the foil is further raised, the pull eventually reaches its highest value corresponding to the minimum receding angle and remains constant on further withdrawal. If the foil is gradually immersed in the liquid, the pull decreases until the maximum advancing angle is reached. If the initial θ is obtuse, it may become acute during withdrawal, that is capillary pull may change its direction from out of to into the liquid; and if the initial θ is acute, it may turn obtuse when the foil is pushed into the liquid.

§21. THE DIFFERENCE between the maximum advancing and the minimum receding contact angle (θ_A and θ_R, respectively) is either zero or positive. It is equal to zero when $\theta_A = 0$, that is when the liquid spontaneously spreads over the solid in a thin film; in this instance also $\theta_R = 0$ and there is no hysteresis. The difference $\theta_A - \theta_R$ may be small (say, 3°) when the solid is particularly smooth and does not swell in the liquid. When the solid is not very smooth, or imbibes some liquid, or both, $\theta_A - \theta_R$ is likely to be great; a hysteresis of wetting amounting to 90° is not at all rare.

The dependence of hysteresis on surface roughness and swelling is readily understood if the probable mechanisms of the effect are considered. Three such mechanisms are recognized.

1. The first is believed to be operative when there is no intermixing between the solid and the liquid and no macroscopic shift of the 3-phase boundary; it is caused by rugosity alone. Figure 22 represents a point of the 3-phase boundary and its

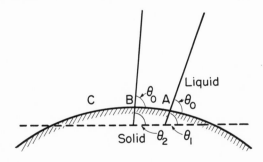

FIG. 22. Hysteresis of wetting caused by surface roughness.

immediate surroundings. The shaded part is a hill on the solid surface. The true contact angle, i.e., the angle θ_0 between air, liquid, and the true solid surface at a given point, is set equal to 80° in the sketch. The apparent angle, i.e., that between the tangent to the drop and the main plane (discontinuous line) of the solid, is θ_1. When a small volume of the liquid is added to the drop (which is situated to the right of A), the liquid surface moves from A to B, the true contact angle is believed to remain constant, and consequently the apparent angle increases from θ_1 to θ_2. The shift of the 3-phase line from A to B is too small to be noticed without special instruments. When the 3-phase line, on a further addition of liquid to the drop, moves to the left of the summit (to C), its position can be shown to become instable and the drop expands until the 3-phase boundary reaches or overshoots the bottom of the groove.

2. There is still no intermixing but the drop slides along an inclined plane or a plate is pulled out of a liquid. The liquid present in the grooves of the solid behind the receding 3-phase line cannot keep pace with its main volume, see §§5 and 14. Thus a liquid ribbon remains in the wake of the drop. The rear of the drop acquires a shape illustrated in Fig. 23 and the apparent contact angle may be immeasurably small. When the motion of the drop continues, the ribbon must be extended or ruptured, and the resistance of the ribbon seems to be the main component of the friction observed at every sliding of the 3-phase boundary.

3. When the solid swells in, or is in any other manner modified by, the liquid, the front of a moving drop (or a moving meniscus) is in contact with the unaltered solid, while its rear is in contact with the swollen (generally: modified) material. Obviously, the advancing and the receding contact angles must in general be different and θ_R be smaller than θ_A, see §16.

Fig. 23. Hysteresis of wetting caused by liquid remaining behind a sliding drop.

Rate of Wetting. Removal of Air

§22.   LIQUID ADHESIVE usually is spread during the application over the whole surface to be joined. This operation, however, does not secure displacement of air from the depressions, crevices etc. present on the surface, §3. This displacement is achieved by capillary forces and retarded by the viscosity (or more generally, consistency) of the liquid.

The magnitude and direction of capillary forces are given by Laplace's equation of capillary pressure P_c:

$$P_c = \gamma \left(\frac{1}{R_1} + \frac{1}{R_2} \right);\qquad(2)$$

γ is surface tension and R_1 and R_2 are the two main radii of curvature. Pressure rises by P_c every time when liquid surface is crossed from the convex to the concave side.

For viscous forces, in the simplest group of substances, Newton's formula

$$\tau = \eta(du/dx)\qquad(3)$$

is valid; τ is shearing stress acting in every plane parallel to the liquid motion and directed opposite to this movement; η is viscosity; u is linear velocity in direction z (normal to the plane of the paper, see Fig. 24), and x is distance in a direction perpendicular to z. In a narrow slit schematically represented in Fig. 24, every volume of liquid 1 cm. long (in the y direction), 1 cm. deep (in the z direction), and dx cm. wide is subjected to a viscous force $\eta(du/dx)$ at its left and $\eta[(du/dx) + (d^2u/dx^2)\,dx]$ at its right boundary, the resultant force being $\eta(d^2u/dx^2)\,dx$. When liquid moves *without acceleration*, this viscous force is counterbalanced by a force originating from the pressure gradient along the z axis; if this gradient is $\Delta P/\Delta z$, the force on the above described liquid volume is $(\Delta P/\Delta z)\,dx$. From the equation

$$\eta\,\frac{d^2u}{dx^2} = \frac{\Delta P}{\Delta z}\qquad(4)$$

it is clear that, as long as $\Delta P/\Delta z$ is constant, d^2u/dx^2 also is constant in the liquid vein under consideration and, consequently, $u = f(x)$ is a parabola. Thus,

$$u = a + bx + cx^2,$$

a, b, and c being constants. Obviously, $c = (1/2\eta)(\Delta P/\Delta z)$. At

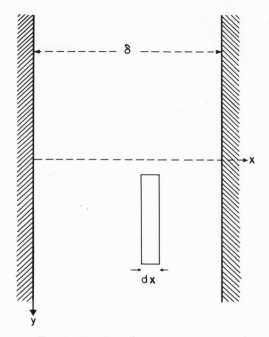

Fɪɢ. 24. Laminar flow in a narrow slit.

$x = 0$, see Fig. 24, $u = 0$ because there is no slippage between solid and liquid, §5; hence, $a = 0$. At $x = \delta/2$, i.e., in the plane of symmetry, from symmetry reasons $du/dx = 0$; hence $b = -c\delta = -(\delta/2\eta)(\Delta P/\Delta z)$. Thus,

$$u = -\frac{1}{2\eta} \cdot \frac{\Delta P}{\Delta z}\,(\delta x - x^2). \tag{5}$$

The volume of liquid moving through the cross section of the slit along 1 cm. of its length per second is

$$-\int_0^\delta u \cdot dx = \frac{\delta^3}{12\eta} \cdot \frac{\Delta P}{\Delta z} \tag{6}$$

and the mean linear velocity is

$$u_m = \frac{\delta^2}{12\eta} \cdot \frac{\Delta P}{\Delta z}. \tag{7}$$

When pressure difference causing liquid flow in the crack is due to capillarity, $2\gamma \cos \theta_A/\delta$ must be substituted for ΔP. This is made clear by Fig. 25, in which the slit of Fig. 24 is shown

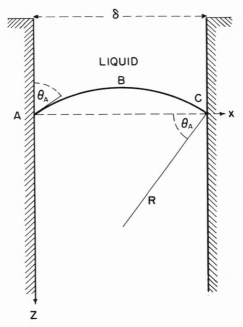

FIG. 25. Flow of liquid into a narrow plane-parallel slit.

in a section perpendicular to the axis of y. The liquid is shown in the upper part of the slit, and its curved meniscus is supposed to advance toward increasing z values. For narrow clearances, gravitation may be neglected in comparison with capillarity; thus the meniscus may be approximated as a part of a cylindrical surface, the axis of the cylinder being normal to the paper and line ABC being an arc of a circle. One of the radii of curvature, see equation (2), namely that situated in the plane parallel to y and z, is infinitely great. The other radius is in the plane including x and z axes; it is indicated by letter R in the sketch. It is seen that $\delta = 2R \cdot \cos \theta_A$, if θ_A is the maximum advancing angle (as the meniscus is supposed to advance). Hence, $1/R = 2 \cos \theta_A/\delta$; equation (2) then affords

$$P_c = 2\gamma \cdot \cos \theta_A/\delta.$$

This pressure difference exists between the meniscus and the crack orifice; if their momentary distance is z, this value has to be substituted for Δz in equation (7). Writing also dz/dt for u_m (t is time), we obtain

$$z \frac{dz}{dt} = \frac{\delta}{6\eta} \cdot \gamma \cos \theta_A \qquad (8)$$

and, after integration,

$$z_0{}^2 = \frac{\delta\gamma \cos \theta_A}{3\eta} t, \qquad (9)$$

z_0 being z at the bottom of the crack.

Equation (9) can be written in dimensionless form. Let u be the average velocity of the advance of the meniscus, that is $u = z_0/t$. Then

$$\frac{z_0}{\delta} = \frac{\gamma \cos \theta_A}{3\eta u}. \qquad (10)$$

The ratio of $\gamma \cos \theta$ to ηu is a pure number because γ is measured in g.sec.$^{-2}$, η in g. cm.$^{-1}$sec.$^{-1}$, and u in cm. sec.$^{-1}$. This ratio is important in all phenomena determined by an interplay of surface tension and viscosity, see §29. To emphasize the importance of time, it can also be written

$$\frac{\gamma \cos \theta_A t}{\eta l}, \qquad (11)$$

t being the time alloted to the experiment and l the length of the meniscus advance.

In this paragraph, an estimate is made of the time needed to fill a long crevice δ cm. wide and z_0 cm. deep. An aqueous liquid adhesive usually will have surface tension of about 70 g./sec.^{2} while the γ of an organic adhesive will be nearer to 30 g./sec.^{2}. The viscosity in the moment of application is likely to be somewhere between 0.01 and 100 g./cm. sec.; thus the range of viscosities is much wider than that of surface tensions. Consider a crevice whose depth is $\sqrt{16.7}$ times its width (i.e., $z_0^2 = 16.7 \ \delta^2$) and assume $\gamma \cos \theta_A = 50$ g./sec.[2] Some values are calculated on this basis in Table IV.

Table IV
Time to Fill a Crevice, in sec.

δ cm.	$\eta = 0.01$	1	100 g./cm.sec.
10^{-5}	10^{-7}	10^{-5}	10^{-3}
10^{-3}	10^{-5}	10^{-3}	10^{-1}
10^{-1}	10^{-3}	10^{-1}	10

If the crack has a V shape, see Fig. 26, time t needed for filling is, approximately, given by equation

$$z_0 \ln \frac{z_0}{z_0 - z} - z = \frac{\delta_0 \gamma \cos \theta_A}{6 \eta z_0} t. \tag{12}$$

In theory, the crack will never be completely filled but as, in reality, the wedge will be blunt near the apex, the delay will not be dangerous; if, for instance, the bottom is reached at $z = 0.9 \ z_0$, equation (12) is transformed into

$$1.40 \ z_0^2 = \frac{\delta_0 \gamma \cos \theta_A}{6 \eta} t$$

which is sufficiently similar to equation (9).

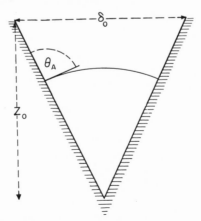

Fig. 26. Flow of liquid into a V-shaped groove.

Time of filling can be great when cos θ_A is small, that is θ_A is approximately 90°. As the maximum advancing contact angle is larger, and can be much larger, than the equilibrium contact angle θ, see §21, θ should not be permitted to exceed, say, 10° and $\theta = 0$ should always be aspired to. When θ_A is greater than 90°, cos θ_A is negative and the meniscus tends to get out of any depression. In these instances, air can be removed by applying a vacuum, but this artifice apparently has not been well tested and cannot be relied upon.

§23.   As FAR AS the intended removal of air from the surface of an adherend by the liquid adhesive is concerned, the above review of wetting phenomena leads to the following main conclusions.

1. Good wetting, i.e., an equilibrium contact angle of zero or near zero, is essential.

2. Because of the sensitivity of contact angles to impurities, the experimenter should not rely on general statements such as "solid A is perfectly wetted by liquid B." This may be true as a rule, but accidental contamination of A in a particular instance may be sufficient to prevent its perfect wetting.

3. Usually, air can be displaced by a liquid adhesive if this contains a solvent of a low surface tension, see §16. However, there is no guarantee that, when the solvent evaporates, the solid ingredients of the adhesive rather than air will take its place; see §42.

4. Surface roughness, generally speaking, does not markedly retard the displacement of air.

§24.   IT IS IMPLIED in the treatment of §22 that, when liquid advances into a valley, air initially present there can escape without experiencing any serious resistance. This assumption presumably is correct as long as the actual displacement of air from the solid surface is considered. However, as soon as this displaced air has formed a bubble fully surrounded by the liquid, surface forces cease to affect its position or its motion, and the bubble can be eliminated from the system only by gravitation or by the moving liquid itself.

The motion of bubbles caused by gravitation may be too slow and often is in a wrong direction. The rate u of ascent of bubbles can crudely be calculated from Stokes' equation

$$u = \frac{2}{9\eta} \, g\rho r^2; \tag{13}$$

g is acceleration due to gravity, ρ is density of liquid minus density of air, and r is the radius of the rising sphere. The equation is not exactly applicable to bubbles because they are not spherical and because the motion considered in equation (13) is not the only one taking place during the ascent. If $\rho = 1$ g./cm.^{3}, $r = 0.01$ cm., and $\eta = 1$ g./cm.sec., equation (13) affords u of approximately 0.02 cm./sec., and if $\rho = 1$, $r = 0.001$ cm. and $\eta = 10$, then $u = 0.00002$ cm./sec. Thus, small bubbles will not travel far in many commercial adhesives during the short time when these are still liquid.

Depending on the kind and the position of an adhint, see §2, movement in the gravitational field may be beneficial or detrimental. Thus, if the adherend surfaces are vertical, bubbles will tend to rise between them and to escape; but if these surfaces are horizontal and nonporous, bubbles adjacent to the upper surface will not move and those originating from the lower surface will join them, thus creating an agglomeration of bubbles and, consequently, a weak layer at the upper boundary of the adhesive film. Observations confirming this description probably have been made by many people experienced in adhints but quantitative studies of the effect seem to be lacking. If at least the upper adherend is porous, bubbles may escape through it.

§25.   DISPLACEMENT of bubbles with the excess of the adhesive probably is the most common method of their removal. As long as the bubbles are small and not too numerous, they do not significantly upset the pattern of flow of the liquid adhesive when its excess is being squeezed out by the outside pressure. A calculation of this flow is given here in some detail because it is important not only for bubble elimination but also for (the simplest instance of) tackiness, §31.

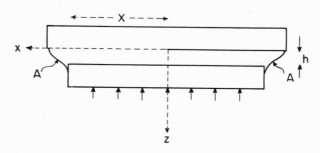

FIG. 27. Squeezing of liquid between two parallel plates.

Consider two parallel rectangular plates, as in Fig. 27; the lower plate is pressed upward with force F. The liquid adhesive between the plates will gradually be forced out. We assume that whatever happens to the adhesive outside the slit between the plates is of no importance; or, in other words, that only a negligible fraction of force F is used up on changing the shape and position of the excess adhesive A, A.

Force F is needed to overcome the viscous forces in the adhesive during its flow. Assume the adhesive to have a viscosity η independent of the rate of flow as in §22. Let, for simplicity's sake, the plates be so long in the y direction (normal to x and z) that the flow along this direction may be disregarded in comparison with that along the x axis. Denote the pressure on the plate, that is F divided by the area of the plate, by letter f. As liquid flows between two parallel plates, equation (6) is valid here; to conform to Fig. 27 we write it as volume velocity $= (h^3/12\eta)(dP/dx)$. Another expression for this quantity is arrived at as follows. The volume of liquid between the median plane (in which $x = 0$) and the plane of any other x is xh per unit length of the plate (in the y direction); h is the variable distance between the plates. Thus, volume of liquid flowing outward through any x plane (per unit length of y) is $-x(dh/dt)$, t being time. Hence,

$$x \frac{dh}{dt} = -\frac{h^3}{12\eta} \cdot \frac{dP}{dx}. \tag{14}$$

Equation (14) is concerned only with the movement parallel to the x axis; obviously there must be some movement of the liquid upward from the vicinity of the rising plate, but we neglect it here.

Abbreviate

$$\frac{12\eta}{h^3} \cdot \frac{dh}{dt} = 2\,K; \tag{15}$$

this quantity is independent of x. Consequently,

$$-\frac{dP}{dx} = 2\,Kx$$

can be integrated to $P = -Kx^2 + K_1$. The integration constant K_1 is found from the condition that the pressure at the edge of the plates must be equal to the atmospheric pressure. If only the excess of the pressure in the liquid over that outside is counted, then $P = 0$ at $x = X$, if X is the half-width of the plates. Thus $K_1 = KX^2$ and

$$P = K(X^2 - x^2). \tag{16}$$

As long as liquid flows with a negligible acceleration, the integral $\displaystyle\int_0^X P\,dx$ must be equal to Xf. Thus,

$$Xf = K \int_0^X (X^2 - x^2)\,dx = \frac{2}{3}\,KX^3 \tag{17}$$

or

$$K = \frac{3}{2}\,\frac{f}{X^2} \tag{18}$$

Substituting (18) into (15), we obtain

$$\frac{dh}{h^3} = \frac{f}{4\eta X^2}\,dt, \tag{19}$$

whence

$$\frac{1}{h_2^2} - \frac{1}{h_1^2} = \frac{ft}{2\eta X^2} \quad\text{or}\quad ft = 2\eta X^2\left(\frac{1}{h_2^2} - \frac{1}{h_1^2}\right). \tag{20}$$

Equation (20) permits calculation of the time needed for pressure f to diminish the distance between the plates from h_1 to h_2. Three numerical examples will illustrate the meaning of equation (20).

1. $f = 10^6$ baryes (i.e., approximately 14 psi), $\eta = 1$ g./cm. sec., $X = 1$ cm., $h_1 = 0.1$ cm., $h_2 = 0.01$ cm. Time $t = 0.02$ sec.

2. $f = 10^5$ baryes (i.e., approximately 1.4 psi), $\eta = 10$ g./cm. sec., $X = 10$ cm., $h_1 = 0.1$ cm., $h_2 = 0.01$ cm. Time $t = 198$ sec.

3. $f = 10^5$ baryes, $\eta = 10$ g./cm.sec., $X = 10$ cm., $h_1 = 0.1$ cm., $h_2 = 0.001$ cm. Time $t = 19,998$ sec.

If the plates are circular rather than rectangular and a is their radius, equation (21) results:[8,9]

$$ft = \frac{3}{4}\,\eta a^2 \left(\frac{1}{h_2{}^2} - \frac{1}{h_1{}^2} \right) \tag{21}$$

or

$$Ft = \frac{3}{4}\,\pi\eta a^4 \left(\frac{1}{h_2{}^2} - \frac{1}{h_1{}^2} \right), \tag{22}$$

as in this instance $F = \pi a^2 f$. When $h_2 \ll h_1$,

$$ft = \frac{3}{4}\,\eta\,\frac{a^2}{h_2{}^2} \tag{23}$$

and

$$Ft = \frac{3}{4}\,\pi\eta\,\frac{a^4}{h_2{}^2}. \tag{24}$$

Any of the relations (21) to (24) is referred to as Stefan's equation. A comparison of (20) and (21) demonstrates that the radius of a circular plate in this phenomenon is equivalent to $\sqrt{8/3}\,X$.

If the plates are elliptical, with the half-axes a and b, then

$$Ft = \frac{3\pi\eta a^3 b^3}{2(a^2 + b^2)} \left(\frac{1}{h_2{}^2} - \frac{1}{h_1{}^2} \right); \tag{25}$$

the equation given by Reynolds[10] has another numerical factor and must be the result of an error in calculation.

For the limits of validity of the reasoning presented in this section see §§31 to 35.

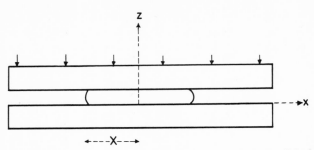

FIG. 28. Spreading of a drop by pressure between two parallel plates.

If the adhesive initially was present as a drop between the two adherends, see Fig. 28, time t is needed to spread the adhesive over the whole surface by pressing the plates together. Let again the mathematically simplest instance be considered, namely gradual spreading of a drop very long in the y direction (normal to the plane of the paper) and short in the x direction. Equations (15) and (16) are still valid but now the half-width of the drop, that is X, is a function of the distance h between the plates. Let V be the constant volume of the drop spread over the length l in the y direction. Then, whatever the value of t,

$$V = hXl. \tag{26}$$

Analogously to (17),

$$F = Kl \int_0^X (X^2 - x^2)\, dx = \frac{2}{3} KX^3 l. \tag{27}$$

When (26) is combined with (27), equation

$$K = \frac{3Fh^3l^2}{2V^3} \tag{28}$$

results. Its comparison with equation (15) affords

$$\frac{4\eta}{h^3} \frac{dh}{dt} = \frac{Fh^3l^2}{V^3}. \tag{29}$$

Integration leads to

$$\frac{1}{h_2{}^5} - \frac{1}{h_1{}^5} = \frac{5}{4} \frac{Fl^2}{\eta V^3}\, t, \tag{30}$$

if again h_1 is the initial and h_2 the final distance between the plates. Usually, $h_1 \gg h_2$ and $(1/h_1{}^5)$ may be neglected in comparison with $(1/h_2{}^5)$. In the final state, $F = flX_2 = fV/h_2$, if X_2 is the final width of the drop and f is the average pressure as in equation (20). Thus,

$$ft = \frac{4\eta V^2}{5h_2{}^4 l^2} = \frac{4}{5}\frac{\eta X_2{}^2}{h_2{}^2} = \frac{4\eta X_2{}^4 l^2}{5V^2}. \tag{31}$$

The second form of equation (31) is strikingly similar to equation (20).

If the plates are circular,

$$Ft = \frac{3\eta V^2}{8\pi}\left(\frac{1}{h_2{}^4} - \frac{1}{h_1{}^4}\right). \tag{32}$$

If a is the radius of the plates, $V = \pi a^2 h_2$ at the moment when the drop has spread over the whole plate area. Hence, neglecting $1/h_1{}^4$ in comparison with $1/h_2{}^4$,

$$Ft = \frac{3\pi\eta a^4}{8h_2{}^2}; \tag{33}$$

here[11] the product Ft is one-half that given by equation (24).

§26. THE EXACT MECHANISM of the elimination of air dislodged from the adherend surface must depend on the porosity (or its absence) of the adherends and on the mode of application of the adhesive, but apparently no systematic study of the phenomenon has been made yet.

A particularly simple experiment on the effect of bubble removal by the adhesive flow may be described here.[12] Polyethylene powder was spread on an aluminum foil either along the periphery of a rectangle, see Fig. 29b, or along its middle as in Fig. 29a, a glass plate was placed on each foil, and the sandwiches were heated above the melting range of the polyethylene under a small pressure. It is clear that in the arrangement of Fig. 29b air is likely to be trapped between aluminum, glass, and the wall of molten polyethylene, while in the other arrangement spreading melt will readily push air out of the clearance between foil and plate. In accord with the expectation, joints of the a-kind showed no large bubbles after setting, while the b-type joints had visible

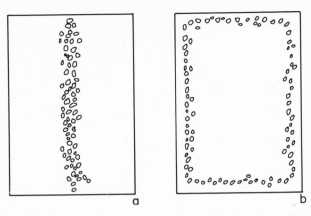

Fig. 29. Importance of air removal in the application of an adhesive. In *b* air was entrapped, and in *a* its escape was easy. From reference 12.

bubbles the largest of which was 0.8 cm. long. The peeling resistance of the b joints was 1.6×10^5 and 1.9×10^5, and that of the a joints 2.6×10^5 and 3.6×10^5 dynes per centimeter width.

A similar observation was made by Bredzs.[13] Two horizontal steel cylinders were placed along one axis so that the clearance between the two bases facing each other was a fraction of a millimeter thick. Then a loop of solder wire was put around the clearance and the system was heated. The solder melted and advanced into the slit because of capillary pressure. However, since penetration occurred simultaneously along the whole periphery, an air bubble remained entrapped near the center of the clearance thus giving rise to weak joints. To prevent void formation, the axial part of the steel cylinders was kept hotter than the peripheral part, and the solder was maintained at a temperature high enough, i.e., at a viscosity low enough, for the bubble to escape because of gravitation.

In some special instances removal of air is achieved by submerging the two adherends in a liquid. Thus, the safety glass of 20 years ago was made in an "assembly bath" (see, e.g., reference 14) of dimethyl phthalate or a similar liquid, in which the two glass plates and the cellulose acetate interlayer were pressed together.

Pretreatment of Adherend Surfaces

§27.   USUALLY AIR is not the only substance which would
give rise to a weak boundary layer if not removed before the
application of the adhesive. Every liquid, every powder, and
every solid of a lesser mechanical strength than the adherend and
the glue would act as air does. The composition of this surface
impurity clearly depends on the solid but is just as much influenced by the particulars of the latter's manufacture and
handling. Thus, each case must be considered on its own merit.
However, science and experience still can help the experimenter.

Science indicates which of the impurities are, and which are
not detrimental. Liquids, powders, and weak solids mentioned
in the preceding paragraph belong to the first, and strong solids
to the second group. Thus, aluminum powder on an aluminum
surface would not be a foreign matter in the chemical sense but
it must be removed for preparing a strong adhint. On the other
hand, aluminum oxide on aluminum, §8, obviously is an "impurity" but there is no need for eliminating it as long as organic
adhesives are employed because apparently no polymer yet was
capable of breaking the natural alumina film on the metal.

Experience teaches us what impurities are likely to be present
on a commercial solid, whose manufacturing methods are known,
and how these impurities have been successfully removed before Information of this kind can be found in many papers and
company reports and also in the oral tradition, but unfortunately
very few systematic comparisons of various treatments were performed, and those that were were made either without any regard
to a theory or under the influence of a theory which is believed incorrect by the author of this book. As a result, we know only
that a particular treatment of a given adherend was beneficial
but we do not know whether all the steps of this treatment were
really needed, whether another treatment would have produced
an even stronger adhint, and so on.

In the literature often statements similar to the following
quotation[15] occur: "It is easiest to attach rubber to steel, brass,
cast iron, and aluminum alloys. It is difficult to make it adhere

to stainless steel, bronzes, and magnesium alloys, and particularly difficult—to tin-containing bronzes." This observation may mean that removal of detrimental surface impurities from commercial steel, etc., has been sufficiently standardized while no satisfactory procedure for the analogous cleaning of tin bronzes was found as yet; or its meaning may be that a weak boundary layer forms in an interaction between tin bronze and the adhesive during the setting of the latter, see §49, while steel does not give rise to an analogous reaction. The stress concentration effect of Chapter VII is less likely in this instance.

Obviously, additional experiments guided by correct theory are needed. Guessing at present is made particularly unprofitable because experiences of different investigators often disagree. Thus, Zherebkov[15] advocates degreasing and sandblasting for all metals (to be attached to rubber) and stresses the importance of roughening the metal surfaces, while, in an almost simultaneous publication, Abbey[16] insists on a mirror finish of the metal parts (to which rubber will be glued), warns against sand blasting to which grit blasting is preferred, and recommends chemical pickling of aluminum alloys (in a sodium carbonate solution), magnesium alloys (in a chromic acid solution), zinc (in 15% phosphoric acid), and brass (in a solution of zinc oxide in concentrated sulfuric and concentrated nitric acid). Comparisons of mechanical and chemical treatment of aluminum alloys prior to glueing can be found in literature[17] and one is illustrated in Fig. 104, §95.

Examples of the effect of surface treatment on the final strength of adhints are tabulated in this section. Table V gives uncorrected breaking stresses of butt joints "steel–an isocyanate adhesive–natural rubber" and "steel–isocyanate adhesive–Neoprene."[15] Table VI reproduces some data [18] for lap joints of an aluminum alloy made with four commercial adhesives; the second column of the table shows the observed range of uncorrected breaking stresses for all four adhesives, and the third column indicates the apparent percentage of improper joints, §15.

TABLE V.

BREAKING STRESS AND SURFACE TREATMENT. STEEL ADHERENDS

Surface treatment	Breaking stress in bars	
	Natural rubber	Neoprene
Sand blasting	60.4	81.0
Machining	27.5	22.6
Grinding	24.0	36.7
Acid etching	53.2	61.8

TABLE VI

BREAKING STRESS AND SURFACE TREATMENT. ALUMINUM ADHERENDS

Surface treatment	Breaking stress in bars	Percentage of improper joints
Alkaline detergent, anodizing in chromic acid, heating in water	31–145	80–100%
Alkaline detergent, anodizing in sulfuric acid, "pore sealing"	176–213	0– 69%
Immersion in $Na_2Cr_2O_7$ solution in sulfuric acid	170–332	2– 40%

Presumably, the indication of the surface treatment given in Tables V and VI is not at all meaningful. For instance, sand blasting may be expected to result in different effects according to whether the sand was or was not heated to destroy organic impurities. Also the roughening achieved by sand blasting may or may not be important according to the amount of the adhesive used. Suppose, for instance, that the experimenter standardizes this amount so as to have an adhesive film of the average thickness of 20 microns. If the h_{max}, §3, of the adherends is, say, 5 microns, the clearance would be filled with the adhesive and a proper joint may result, but if h_{max} is raised to 100 microns by sandblasting, a "starved" joint containing many voids will be obtained. On the other hand, if the adhesive amount is not standardized and the experimenter uses ten times as much glue on the rough as on the smooth surface, the effect of roughness may appear negligible.

Analogous remarks can be made in reference to the other procedures. Thus, if heating in water was the last treatment accorded to an aluminum part, the breaking stress of an adhint will depend on how well water was removed before the application of the adhesive, on the purity of the water used, and so on.

§28.   IN THIS SECTION some better studied examples of surface treatment and surface contamination are reported.

Chromic acid treatment of magnesium alloys is mentioned in §27. When an alloy containing 4% Zn and 1% Ce was treated with a hot alkaline chromate solution and then glued with "Metlbond 4021" (composition unknown), adhints of a very low peel strength resulted and failure occurred cohesively in the chromate coating.[19]

As mentioned in §27, rubber is said better to adhere to brass than to many other metals. However, failures of the brass-rubber bond were common. Buchan[20] examined brass electrodeposits which gave rise to weak joints and found that they (a) either were mineralogically nonuniform (that is, consisted of α-brass in some and of β-brass in the other spots), (b) or contained cavities, (c) or were chemically impure (for instance, contaminated with zinc oxide or copper oxides). A particularly striking impurity consisted of the salt $[Zn(NH_3)_6]$ $[Zn_3(Fe(CN)_6)_2]$.[20,21] The bath contained no deliberately introduced iron, but the amounts of iron dissolved out of the tools used were sufficient to cause precipitation of this complex salt at the brass surface during electroplating.

Sensitivity of electrodeposited coating to impurities may also be illustrated by another example.[22] In the electroplating of nickel on some other metal, a brief interruption of current may ruin the adherence of the subsequent deposit. As soon as the electrostatic field near the cathode surface disappears, non-ionic ingredients of the solution become adsorbed on this surface and form a weak boundary layer.

How small are the amounts of impurities sufficient to affect the strength of adhints is exemplified by Fig. 30 based on some published results.[23] Butt joints of steel–poly(vinyl acetate)–steel, at a glue line thickness, §15, of 0.0025 cm., had breaking stresses of approximately 486 bars. When decanoic acid was deposited on one of the steel surfaces before the application of the adhesive and the system "contaminated steel-poly(vinyl

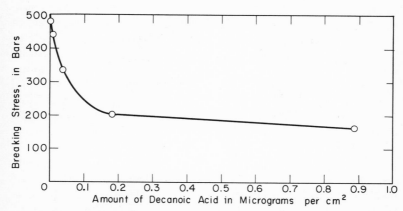

FIG. 30. Effect of decanoic acid on the strength of steel-poly(vinyl acetate) adhints. Abscissa: amount of decanoic acid per unit area, in micrograms/cm.². Ordinate: breaking stress in bars. Data of reference 23.

acetate)–steel" kept above the melting range of the adhesive for an hour, the breaking stress was smaller the greater the degree of contamination. As the numbers along the abscissa of the figure indicate, considerable changes are caused by amounts as small as 10^{-8} g./cm.²; one touch of a finger may easily transfer greater quantities of finger grease. When the above system was maintained above the freezing temperature of poly(vinyl acetate) for a longer time, decanoic acid (or iron decanoate) apparently gradually dissolved in the liquid adhesive and, consequently, was losing its ability to form a weak boundary layer. Thus, at glue line thickness of 0.010 cm. and total amount of $C_{10}H_{20}O_2$ equal to 8.9×10^{-7} g./cm.², the breaking stress was 207, 268, 321, and 471 bars when the heating time was zero, 1 hour, 2 hours, or extrapolated to infinity. At a constant total amount of acid and a constant heating time, the effect of the acid was greater the thinner the adhesive film.

When a little over 2×10^{-7} g. stearic acid was deposited on one square cm. of a stainless steel surface, the breaking stress of steel–ice adhints at $-20°$ was lowered from about 28 to about 6 bars.[24] For other examples see reference 25 and §32.

In all probability, extremely small quantities of foreign substances on an adherend surface can also enhance the strength of an adhint. Suppose, for instance, that a material such as decanoic acid was present, unnoticed, on the surface before treatment. If the surface is now contaminated with a minute amount of a substance which (a) reacts with decanoic acid and (b) gives with it a reaction product readily miscible with poly (vinyl acetate), the acid will be removed from the surface while the adhesive is still in molten state, and the breaking stress will correspond to the highest point on the curve of Fig. 30.

In plastics reinforced with glass fibers, the fibers usually are coated with a "finish" before they are immersed in the plastic material in its uncured state; see, e.g., reference 26. If these "finishes" strengthen the adherence between glass and polymer, they presumably act as indicated in the foregoing paragraph. Apparently, the surface of glass filaments often contains an ingredient (which may be simply water) which adversely affects the wettability of the filaments by the liquid polymer. The "finishes" seem to displace these ingredients or to depress their action thus facilitating penetration of the resin in the capillaries between the filaments.[27,28]

REFERENCES

1. Fox, H. W., and Zisman, W. A., *J. Colloid Sci.* **7**, 109 (1952).
2. Bartell, F. E., and Bristol, K. E., *J. Phys. Chem.* **44**, 86 (1940).
3. Bikerman, J. J., *Ind. Eng. Chem., Anal. Ed.*, **13**, 443 (1941).
4. Blaisdell, B. E., *J. Math. and Phys.* **19**, 186 (1940).
5. Voet, A., and van Elteren, J. F., *Rec. trav. chim.* **56**, 923 (1937).
6. Shafrin, E. G., and Zisman, W. A., *J. Colloid Sci.* **4**, 571 (1949).
7. Bikerman, J. J., "Surface Chemistry," 2nd ed. Academic Press, New York, 1958.
8. Stefan, J., *Sitzber. Akad. Wiss. Wien, Math.-naturw. Kl.* **69**, 713 (1874).
9. Bikerman, J. J., *J. Colloid Sci.* **2**, 163 (1947).
10. Reynolds, O., *Phil. Trans. Roy. Soc. London* **177** I, 157 (1886).
11. Healey, A, *Trans. Inst. Rubber Ind.* **1**, 334 (1926).
12. Bikerman, J. J., *J. Appl. Polymer Sci.* **2**, 216 (1959).
13. Bredzs, N., *Welding J.* **33**, 545-s (1954).
14. Waine, A. C., *in* "Adhesion," p. 41. Soc. Chem. Ind., London 1952.
15. Zherebkov, S. K., "Attachment of Rubber to Metals," p. 16. [Russ.] GNTIKhL., Moscow, 1956.
16. Abbey, W. F., *Rubber World* **134**, 87 (1956).

17. Winter, H., and Krause, G., *Aluminium* **33,** 669 (1957).
18. Eickner, H. W., *U. S. Dept. Agr., Forest Serv., Forest Prod. Lab. No.* **1842** (1954).
19. Hunter, R. J. E., *Can. Aeronaut. J.* **3,** 161 (1957).
20. Buchan, S., "Rubber to Metal Bonding." Crosby Lockwood, London, 1948.
21. Malden, J. W., *Trans. Inst. Rubber Ind.* **27,** 175 (1951).
22. Vagramyan, A. T., and Tsareva, Yu. S., *Doklady Akad. Nauk S.S.S.R.* **74,** 303 (1950).
23. Lasoski, S. W., and Kraus, G., *J. Polymer Sci.* **18,** 359 (1955).
24. Raraty, L. E., and Tabor, D., *Proc. Roy. Soc.* **A245,** 184 (1958).
25. Krotova, N. A., Kirillova, Yu. M., and Deryagin, B. V., *Zhur. Fiz. Khim.* **30,** 1921 (1956).
26. Hinz, W., and Solov, G., *Silikat Tech.* **8,** 178 (1957).
27. McGarry, F. J., *Am. Soc. Testing Materials Bull. No.* **235,** 63 (1959).
28. Bikerman, J. J., and McGarry, F. J., *Glass Ind.* **40,** 525 (1959).

CHAPTER 4

Tack

§29. As SOON AS the clearance between two adherends has been filled with a liquid adhesive, an effort is needed to separate the adherends again. This resistance to separation, manifested by the system when the adhesive is still liquid, has been denoted as *tackiness*. However, the usual meaning of *tack* implies also (a) that only a weak external force was applied when making the joint and (b) that the measurement of the above resistance was made very soon after the application of the adhesive. In §30 the common observation is referred to that two flat solids pressed and wrung together (without any visible adhesive between them) require a considerable force to bring them apart; these solids would not be considered tacky because their contact was achieved after a significant work by the experimenter. If a drop of water is permitted to fall on a horizontal solid plate and the plate is at once turned upside down, the test would comply with the two conditions (a) and (b) and water would be declared non-tacky because gravitational force acting on a large drop is sufficient to cause its downfall.

Properties necessary for a rapid growth of tackiness (as defined in the foregoing paragraph) during the application of an adhesive, that is the properties which make an adhesive tacky, have not been completely determined. The reasoning of §22 seems to offer a suitable starting point. Air can be removed and real contact between adhesive and adherend established, when the ratio $\gamma \cos \theta_A / \eta u$, see formula (11), is large enough. Since product $\gamma \cos \theta_A$ varies from one to another adhesive much less than viscosity η, the value of this ratio depends above all on the product ηu. When the tack of an adhesive is tested, the application of the latter is rapid, that is u is considerable. Hence, η must be small to prevent $\gamma \cos \theta_A / \eta u$ from exceeding the permissible limit. Thus, a low viscosity would favor tack.

On the other hand, see §31, the resistance to separation increases with the viscosity (or consistency) of the adhesive. Hence, a low viscosity would permit rapid establishment of tack but the final value of the latter would be low; see the above example of a water drop. A high viscosity would cause strong resistance to separation but this resistance will require a long time to materialize. Evidently, some compromise value of viscosity would be most advantageous.

Unfortunately, this conclusion must be qualified. None of the commercial adhesives is a Newtonian liquid, that is has one definite value of viscosity (at given temperature and pressure); thus, application of ratio (11) becomes ambiguous. Furthermore, viscosity measurements usually are performed on well-stirred samples, while in the measurement of tack the adhesive is almost undisturbed; in particular, if a thin solid crust is present on the surface of an adhesive tape, the tape will not be tacky although the viscosity of the adhesive spread on the tape backing might have had the optimum magnitude. An adhesive destined for such a tape should have a right viscosity (or, more generally, consistency) and this viscosity should not markedly vary either in time or with the depth of the coating (that is, with the distance from the air–adhesive boundary). Undoubtedly, there are other prerequisites but they have not yet been formulated or made public.

The gradual establishment of good contact between two pieces of a semiliquid adhesive or between such an adhesive and a solid adherend has been followed many times. In all instances the goodness of contact was judged from the resistance of the system to the subsequent separation.

This resistance generally increases with the time of contact and with the pressure during the contact. For a Newtonian liquid in the absence of any perturbations the separation of two plates with a liquid between them is a process exactly inverse to the bringing these plates together, see §22; thus, every increase in the product ft during the squeezing out of the adhesive would cause an equal increase of ft during the separation; t is time and f is the pressure which pushes the plates together or (§31) pulls them apart. In non-Newtonian materials the relation between the resistance to separation on one hand and compression and time on the other is less simple, but as a rule the resistance does increase with f and t.

Thus, when a piece of rubber is cut and the two new surfaces are pressed together by pressure f for time t, the pulling apart is more difficult the greater f and t. For instance,[1] for a natural rubber tire tread, the tackiness (at an arbitrary but constant rate of separation) was 3.5×10^4 dynes/cm.^{2} after $t = 1$ sec. and 15×10^4 dynes/cm.^{2} after $t = 25$ sec. In similar experiments[2] on "butyl rubber" (a copolymer of isobutylene and isoprene) after $t = 6$ sec., tackiness increased by about 20% when f increased from 7×10^5 to 32×10^5 dynes/cm.^{2}. With polyisobutylene, force needed to separate two strips by peeling was 10^5 dynes for 1-cm. width after a contact of 15 minutes and 2.2×10^5 dynes/cm. after 15 hours; and after t = 5 minutes the stripping force was 5×10^4 and 18×10^4 dynes per centimeter when f was 5000 and 50,000 dynes/cm.^{2}, respectively.[3] When both f and t remained constant but the temperature during the contact (not during the subsequent separation) was higher, peeling force was greater, evidently because of the greater mobility of polyisobutylene at higher temperatures; thus this force was, after glueing at 80°, almost twice as great as after glueing at 21°C.[3]

After a prolonged contact, stress needed for separation may be equal to the breaking stress of the rubber tested, that is the two rubber pieces may grow together. This was observed, for instance, by Forbes and McLeod,[4] but the contact time required to reach this maximum strength was different for different rubber compositions (from 3 minutes to 17 hours).

When the tacky material is less solid-like than rubber, tackiness may remain almost constant already after 20 seconds of contact.[5]

§30. The second half of the problem of tack, i.e., the question of the mechanism of resistance to separation, has been more thoroughly investigated.

We may start with the often quoted example of two flat and smooth solid surfaces, which, after being pressed together in air, can be separated only with a considerable effort. Polished steel prisms often called Johansson blocks are choice objects for these tests. Three reasons for the "attraction" between the two surfaces are known.

1. Even when the surface appears clean, it may be contaminated with an oil or with water condensed from the atmosphere. As all solid surfaces, including those of Johansson blocks, are rough, they can touch each other at discrete points only. Let Fig. 31 represent one of these points; the shaded areas

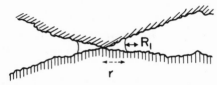

Fig. 31. Droplet of liquid surrounding protuberances on two solid surfaces in contact.

are solids. If there are traces of a liquid between the blocks, they will tend to form droplets around the points of contact because the vapor pressure above a concave meniscus is less than that above a flat or convex liquid surface. If the radius of curvature of the menisci, such as indicated in Fig. 31, is R_1 in the plane of paper and R_2 in a plane normal to it and parallel to the main planes of the solids, the value of R_1 usually will be considerably smaller than that of R_2, and the capillary pressure in the drop will be approximately γ/R_1. The magnitude of R_1 should not be very different from the height of hills in contact; for a polished metal surface we may assume R_1 to be of the order of 10^{-6} cm., see §7. For $\gamma = 50$ g./sec.^{2} and $R_1 = 10^{-6}$ cm., γ/R_1 is 5×10^7 g./cm.sec.^{2} (or 50 bars). The attractive force exerted by the meniscus is approximately $\pi r^2 \gamma/R_1$ because the underpressure γ/R_1 acts on the whole horizontal cross section ($= \pi r^2$) of the drop, Fig. 31. Assume r to be 10^{-4} cm.; the force comes out to be over 1.5 dyne. If there are, say, 600 contact points, the total attractive force would be near 1000 dynes.

Should the volume of the liquid be so great as to form a continuous film between the two surfaces, and if this film is again 10^{-6} cm. thick, the attractive force would be 5×10^7 dynes per each square centimeter of the block surface; γ is again supposed to be 50 g./sec.^{2}.

2. If no fluid of a low electric resistivity is present between or around the blocks, they are mutually attracted because of electrostatic forces, even when the materials of the blocks are supposedly identical. This is caused by the fact that the work function of a solid depends not only on its over-all chemical composition but also on the cleanness of its surface, the crystallographic orientation of its surface layers, and the state of stress of the latter. As it is practically impossible to prepare two surfaces identical in all these respects, one of the two will lose electrons more readily than the other; thus the first body will carry a positive, and the second, a negative charge. These charges, naturally, will be concentrated on the two opposite surfaces and thus give rise to Coulombic attraction between the two blocks. The attraction will lessen if the atmosphere surrounding the blocks is ionized (for instance, by a radioactive substance) or its humidity is high.

§31.   3. THE THIRD of the reasons referred to in the beginning of §30 presumably is the main cause of the tackiness of adhesives and sometimes accounts also for the major part of the difficulty of separating two flat polished solids without an adhesive between them. In §25 the time needed to press two plates together was calculated. An equal time is needed for removing them from each other by reversing the motion; mathematically speaking, we simply exchange the two integration limits. Thus,

$$Ft = \frac{3}{4} \pi \eta a^4 \left(\frac{1}{h_1^2} - \frac{1}{h_2^2} \right) \tag{34}$$

and, in analogy to (23),

$$ft = \frac{3}{4} \eta \frac{a^2}{h_1^2}. \tag{35}$$

In this case the initial clearance (h_1) is smaller than the final (h_2).

In the instance of two polished discs in air, as viscosity of air is about 1.8×10^{-4} g./cm.sec., equation (35) gives $Ft = 1.8 \times 10^{10}$ g.cm./sec. for discs of $a = 2.55$ cm. and $h_1 = 10^{-6}$ cm. Thus, a disc weighing 100 g. would remain suspended in the gravitational field of our earth (which would make F a little smaller than 10^5 g.cm/sec.^{2}) for about 1.8×10^5 seconds (≈ 50 hours). When a liquid adhesive fills the space between the plates, the duration of the disengagement process is much longer. An identical disc in water, instead of air, would continue to hang for 10^7 seconds (i.e., 116 days), the viscosity of water being 0.01 g./cm.sec. at 20°.

An experimental confirmation of equation (34) was supplied by Stefan[6] himself, and results in a satisfactory accord with the theory were obtained several times afterwards; see, for instance, references 7, 8, 9. A few data from the most recent paper[9] may be reproduced here to illustrate the degree of agreement between theory and experiment As the right-hand side of equation (35) is independent of f, the product ft must remain constant when f varies. Table VII corroborates this conclusion.

TABLE VII

PRODUCT ft IS INDEPENDENT OF f.

STEEL PLATES, $h_{rms} = 8 \times 10^{-6}$ CM. PARAFFIN OIL. TEMPERATURE 28.1°

f g./cm.sec.^{2}	135	246	472	736	1060	1715	3830 x 10^2
ft g./cm.sec.	23	23	20	19	20	21	18 x 10^6

As no property of the solid is referred to in equation (35), ft should be independent of the material of the plates; this was verified for nickel, stainless steel, and copper. The temperature coefficient of ft was equal to that of the viscosity of the liquid between the discs; no other quantity appearing in the equation has a temperature coefficient significant in this connection. The magnitude of the initial clearance h_1 was measured directly (as the thickness of the capacitor formed by the two metal discs) and found, within the experimental error, equal to h_1 calculated from the product ft.

The answers given by equations (34) and (35) are, or may be, incorrect when (a) the plates are not immersed, (b) air has not been removed, (c) the solid surfaces are very rough, (d) force F (or rather stress f) is too great or time t is too short, (e) viscosity η is too great, or (f) viscosity is not independent of the rate of shear. These limitations are discussed in the above order in §32 to §35; some of them apply also to the problem of two plates approaching each other, see §25, but are treated here because they are particularly important in the study of tackiness. Some of the experiments on tack were vitiated by trivial mistakes, such as poor alignment and wedge-shaped clearances between the plates, and the effect of these asymmetries is considered in §37.

§32.   (a) WHEN THE PLATES are not immersed or, more exactly, when a meniscus exists around the clearance, capillary pressure acts as indicated in §30. Thus, the value of f to be inserted in, e.g., equation (35) is not the whole external (negative) pressure f but only $f - (2\gamma/h)$ assuming that the liquid perfectly wets the two surfaces; h is the variable distance between the plates. However, this system is analogous to that shown in Fig. 28 rather than to that of Fig. 27 because the area occupied by the liquid varies with time; in §25 it increased; here it, in a symmetrical manner, decreases. Instead of equation (29), equation

$$\frac{4\eta}{h^3}\frac{dh}{dt} = \frac{Fh^3l^2}{V^3} - \frac{2\gamma hl^2}{V^2} \tag{36}$$

is obtained. The integrated expression

$$t = \frac{\eta}{l^2}\left(\frac{F^3V}{2\gamma^5}\right)^{0.5}\arctan\left(\frac{F}{2\gamma V}\right)^{0.5} h + \frac{\eta FV}{2\gamma^2l^2h} + \frac{2\eta V^2}{3\gamma l^2h^3} \tag{37}$$

may at some future date prove useful. For the meaning of the symbols see §25.

(b) The proof reproduced in §25 makes use of the assumption, among others, that the pressure difference P can be relieved only by the centripetal flow of the liquid adhesive. This assumption is invalid if the liquid does not well wet the two (or one of the) solids. In the absence of complete wetting, some air remains between the solid and the liquid, mainly in the valleys on the solid surface. When the external load creates a space of low pressure near the axis of the system, the outside air flows in at the same time as liquid does. As viscosity of air is about one-fiftieth that of water and, perhaps, 0.0001th of that of an industrial adhesive, even a narrow channel open to air and leading toward the center of the plates may cause a marked diminution of the time t of separation. When metal plates were polished with an aqueous abrasive, washed with water, and only superficially dried before being immersed in a hydrocarbon oil (viscosity = 1.9 g./cm. sec.), t was about one-fourth the time observed when the plates were well dried and rinsed with trichloroethylene prior to the application of the oil.[9]

As usual liquid adhesives are more or less saturated with air or may contain volatile solvents, air or solvent vapor will tend to form bubbles near the axis of the joint where the pressure deficiency has the highest value. If these bubbles can grow at a considerable rate, they may relieve the pressure difference in yet another manner.[10,11]

§33. (c) THE EFFECT of surface roughness was studied[9] in an arrangement similar to that of Fig. 27. The lower plate was well polished in all instances while the mean-square-root of the elevations (§3) on the upper plate varied within a wide range. The two plates (with an oil in between) were pressed together with a definite force for a definite time, and both force and time were kept constant, i.e., not adjusted for roughness changes. When, then, loads were suspended from the bottom plate, the product ft proved to be approximately inversely proportional to the height h_{rms} of the upper surface, as determined with a stylus instrument (§3). Figure 32 illustrates this behavior.

Roughness should not be disregarded in the determination of the initial clearance h_1. Thus, it was assumed[12] that, when the two plates are kept "in contact" until the product ft ceases to increase, this limiting value of ft has a molecular significance. In reality[13] the value of h_1 achieved after prolonged contact must be approximately equal to the height of a few tallest hills on the two surfaces; as soon as the upper plate rests on these hills, no further approach to the lower plate is possible, see §5.

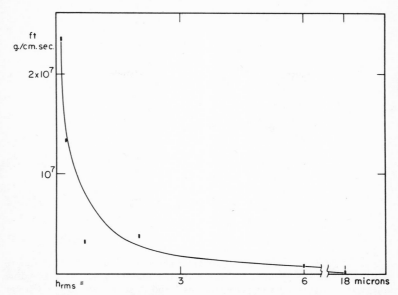

FIG. 32. Dependence of product ft ($=$ stress $\times$ time) on surface roughness for a Newtonian liquid. Abscissa: h_{rms} of the coarse surface, in microns. Ordinate: ft in g./cm. sec. Data of reference 9.

When a horizontal plate slowly descends onto another in a viscous liquid, the distance h between them should be inversely proportional to $\sqrt{t}$, see equation (24). This expectation is fulfilled as long as h is considerably greater than the height of elevations on the two solid surfaces (but, of course, much smaller than the initial distance h_1). When h becomes commensurable with h_{max} (§3), the decrease of h is slowed down. An example of this behavior is presented in Fig. 33 taken from Fuks.[14] Its ordinate is h in microns, its abscissa is $\sqrt{t}$ in seconds, curves 1 and 3 are for a transformer oil apparently between two steel plates, curves 2 and 4 are for 0.01 N aqueous sodium chloride solution apparently between two quartz plates, and the pressure on the upper plate is 0.2 bar for curves 1 and 2, and 4 bars for curves 3 and 4. The leveling off of the curves below about 0.1 micron is undoubtedly due mainly to rugosity but two additional effects may be suspected. The transformer oil apparently con-

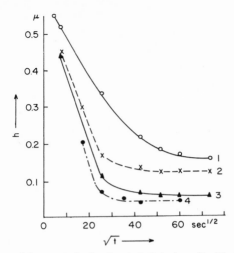

FIG. 33. Rate of descent of a horizontal plate in a liquid. Abscissa: square root of time in sec. Ordinate: distance (in microns) between the descending upper and stationary lower plate. Curves 1 and 3: steel plate in transformer oil. Curves 2 and 4: quartz plate in 0.01 N NaCl solution. Curves 1 and 2: pressure = 0.2 bar. Curves 3 and 4: pressure = 4 bars. From reference 14.

tained impurities which reacted with the steel, and the true viscosity of the liquid next to the adherends was raised by the reaction products. Quartz on the other hand must have swelled in the aqueous solution, see §10, thus forming a very viscous boundary layer. Analogous increases in the true viscosity of the liquid near the intervace presumably take place also when tackiness, i.e., time of separation rather than time of approach, is measured.

Observations similar to those of Fig. 33 have been recorded, for instance, by Needs.[15]

§34.   (d) WHEN THE MUTUAL DETACHMENT of the two plates proceeds too rapidly, i.e., when the applied stress f is too great, equations (34) and (35) cease to be applicable because the liquid flows with an acceleration which cannot be neglected, see §22. This source of error is more dangerous for fluids of a relatively low viscosity, such as water or lubricating oils, than for typical tacky adhesives. For the latter materials, limitation (e) is more important.

(e) When viscosity η is great, the adhesive may have no time to form the parabolic pattern of flow derived in §22 before it ruptures in the manner characteristic for brittle solids. Some kinds of rosin and asphalt are nearly Newtonian liquids, that is their viscosity, although very high, is practically independent of the gradient of velocity as long as this gradient is small, but they break rather than flow if an excessive stress is applied to them. These materials may have viscosity of, say, 1000 g./cm. sec. If $a^2 = 13.33$ cm.^{2} and $h_1^2 = 10^{-8}$ cm.^{2}, equation (35) gives $ft = 10^{12}$ g./cm.sec. Thus, two metal discs of the radius 3.65 cm., glued together with a rosin, would support a stress of 10^{10} g./cm. sec.^{2} (or about 10^4 atmospheres corresponding to approximately 140,000 psi) for 100 seconds. In reality, the tensile stress of such a rosin would be, perhaps, 10^8 g./cm.sec.^{2} and it would crack immediately after the application of the stress.

In less extreme cases, apparently, some flow takes place but instead of being all from the periphery of the adhint toward its axis, it proceeds toward many points or lines. When the detachment is complete, these points remain visible on the adhesive film as protuberances, and the lines are visible as ridges. Call the distance between two nearest protuberances $2a_0$; then equation (35) with a_0 substituted for a, may be used. In other words, we treat the liquid film of radius a as a sum of small films, all in parallel and having each a radius a_0; these elementary films flow independently of their neighbors. As a_0 is likely to be between one-tenth and one-hundredth part of a, the product ft would be 0.01 to 0.0001 that calculated from the original equation. No experimental confirmation of this view is known to the author, however.

§35. (f) WHEN THE VISCOSITY of the adhesive is a function of the rate of shear (or, in another terminology, of the velocity gradient), the physical picture is little changed but mathematical difficulties at once become serious. In this section, consideration is given to only two types of variable viscosity, which are relatively easily amenable to quantitative treatment. Both these types have already been investigated in a very similar manner by Scott.[16]

Figure 34, analogous to Fig. 27, represents the system. If the adhesive is a "Bingham body,"

$$\frac{du}{dz} = \varphi(\tau - \tau_0) \tag{38}$$

instead of $(du/dz) = \tau$, as in a Newtonian liquid, §22. Stress τ_0 (g./cm.sec.^{2}) and quantity φ (cm.sec./g.) are material constants; to account for the rheological behavior of a "Bingham body" both are needed, while in the analogous problems dealing with Newtonian liquids viscosity alone is sufficient. Equation (38) is valid as long as $\tau > \tau_0$; when $\tau \leq \tau_0$, $du/dz = 0$. The viscous stress τ is least, see §22, at $x = X$ and $z = h/2$. In the regions where both these conditions are satisfied, i.e., in the middle between the plates at the edge of the adhesive film, the τ is most likely to be less than τ_0; where $\tau < \tau_0$, u is independent of z; thus the profile of the inflowing liquid (when a tensile force is applied to the plates, see the arrows in Fig. 34) is a truncated parabola (the continuous line) instead of a parabola (dashes) valid for Newtonian liquids.

The viscous force acting on a slab, 1 cm. in the x direction, 1 cm. in the y direction, and dz cm. in the z direction, is $(d\tau/dz)$ dz; as long as flow takes place without acceleration, it is balanced by force $(dp/dx) \cdot l \cdot dz$, p being the difference between the

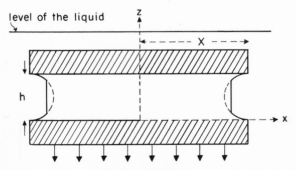

Fig. 34. Separation of two parallel plates in a "Bingham body."

variable pressure in the adhesive and the atmospheric pressure outside. Thus, analogously to (4), we have

$$\frac{d\tau}{dz} = \frac{dp}{dx}. \tag{39}$$

For a Newtonian liquid, dp/dx is independent of z; we assume that this is true also in the present instance. Hence, u is a parabolic function of z as long as τ remains greater than τ_0; if $\tau \leq \tau_0$ between $z = z_0$ and $z = h - z_0$, then $u = u_1 = Az^2 + Bz + C$ between $z = 0$ and $z = z_0$ and between $z = h - z_0$ and $z = h$, and $u = u_0 = $ const. elsewhere. The constants A, B, and C are easily determined by the method sketched in §22; and it is found that

$$u_1 = \frac{\varphi}{2} \frac{dp}{dx} (z^2 - 2zz_0)$$

in the lower half of the clearance,

$$u_1 = \frac{\varphi}{2} \frac{dp}{dx} (z^2 + h^2 + 2zz_0 - 2z_0h - 2hz)$$

in the upper half, and

$$u_0 = - \frac{\varphi}{2} \frac{dp}{dx} z_0^2.$$

The volume V of the adhesive moving from the periphery toward the axis (at $x = 0$) of the system in unit time is

$$V = -2 \int_0^{z_0} u_1 \cdot dz + 2 \int_{z_0}^{h/2} u_0 \cdot dz = y\varphi z_0^2 \frac{dp}{dx} \left(\frac{h}{2} - \frac{z_0}{3} \right),$$

if the depth of the plate (in the y direction, normal to the plane of the paper) is y. Now an approximation is introduced. If the region of constant velocity is thin, the value of $(h/2) - z_0$ is considerably smaller than that of $h/2$; if we neglect $[(h/2) - z_0]^3$ compared with $(h/2)^3$, the above expression is reduced to

$$V = \frac{1}{12} y\varphi \frac{dp}{dx} h^2 \left[h - 3 \left(\frac{h}{2} - z_0 \right) \right].$$

Since

$$\frac{h}{2} - z_0 = \frac{\tau_0}{dp/dx},$$

we may write

$$V = \frac{y\varphi h^3}{12} \frac{dp}{dx} - \frac{y\varphi h^2 \tau_0}{4}. \qquad (40)$$

This quantity must be equal to $yx(dh/dt)$. Hence, p which is zero at $x = X$ and negative everywhere else, is

$$p = \frac{6}{\varphi h^3} \frac{dh}{dt} (x^2 - X^2) + \frac{3\tau_0}{h} (x - X).$$

As the plates are in contact with a liquid layer (i.e., the zone of constant velocity u_0 does not extend to the plates), Pascal's law is still valid and so is the equation

$$F = -y \int_0^X p \cdot dx,$$

F being the external force acting on the right-hand side of the plates. Hence,

$$F = -y \frac{4}{\varphi h^3} \frac{dh}{dt} X^3 + y \frac{3\tau_0}{2h} X^2 \qquad (41)$$

and

$$f = \frac{F}{yX} = \frac{4X^2}{\varphi h^3} \cdot \frac{dh}{dt} + \frac{3\tau_0}{2h} X. \qquad (42)$$

It is seen that equation (19) is obtained if $\tau_0 = 0$ and η is written for $1/\varphi$. Integration of equation (42) affords

$$X \left(\frac{1}{h_1} - \frac{1}{h_2} \right) + \frac{2f}{3\tau_0} \ln \frac{h_2(2fh_1 - 3\tau_0 X)}{h_1(2fh_2 - 3\tau_0 X)} = \frac{3\varphi\tau_0}{8} t. \qquad (43)$$

Obviously, this equation cannot be correct unless f is greater than $3\tau_0 X/2h$; when $f < 3\tau_0 X/2h$, then $dh/dt < 0$, that is no separation occurs, but in this instance the above condition of $\tau_0/(dp/dx)$ being much smaller than $h/2$ is invalid.

If, instead of equation (38),

$$\frac{du}{dz} = \varphi \tau^n \qquad (44)$$

n being a numerical constant, and if $(d\tau/dz) = (dp/dx)$ is again independent of z, then

$$\frac{du}{dz} = \varphi \left(\frac{dp}{dx}\right)^n \left(z - \frac{h}{2}\right)^n$$

and

$$u = \frac{\varphi}{n+1} \left(\frac{dp}{dx}\right)^n \left[\left(z - \frac{h}{2}\right)^{n+1} - \left(\frac{h}{2}\right)^{n+1}\right]$$

for that half of the clearance between $z = (h/2)$ and $z = h$; compare equation (5). The volume

$$V = 2y \frac{\varphi}{n+2} \left(\frac{dp}{dx}\right)^n \left(\frac{h}{2}\right)^{n+2} \qquad (45)$$

must be equal to $yx(dh/dt)$. Hence,

$$p = \frac{2^{(n+1)/n}n(n+2)^{1/n}}{(n+1)\varphi^{1/n}} h^{-(n+2)/n} \left(\frac{dh}{dt}\right)^{1/n}$$
$$[x^{(n+1)/n} - X^{(n+1)/n}]; \qquad (46)$$

if $n = 1$, equation (46) becomes identical with (16), since in this instance $\varphi = (1/\eta)$ and $p = -P$. As $\int_0^X p \cdot dx = Xf$,

$$f = \frac{2^{(n+1)/n} n(n+2)^{1/n}}{(2n+1)\varphi^{1/n}} \cdot h^{-(n+2)/n} \left(\frac{dh}{dt}\right)^{1/n} X^{(n+1)/n}, \qquad (47)$$

see equation (19), and

$$\frac{1}{h_1^{n+1}} - \frac{1}{h_2^{n+1}} = \frac{(n+1)(2n+1)^n}{2^{n+1}(n+2)n^n} \cdot \frac{\varphi f^n t}{X^{n+1}}, \qquad (48)$$

which becomes identical with (20) when $n = 1$.

In some instances,[16a] ft seems to be a function of the complex tensional modulus of the adhesive but the theory of this regularity has not been worked out yet.

§36.   IN §§31 to 35, the rate of detachment normally to the plane of the adhesive film was considered. Often, tackiness is judged by the ease of peeling or stripping a flexible ribbon coated with a tacky adhesive from a rigid plate previously touched by the coated side of the ribbon (of the adhesive tape). Figure 35 illustrates the geometry of the experiment.

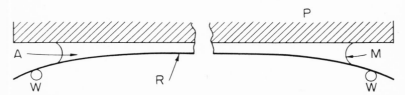

FIG. 35. Peeling in a system consisting of a rigid plate P, a liquid film A and a flexible ribbon R. M = meniscus. From reference 17.

Only the simplest instance (i.e., when the adhesive is a Newtonian liquid) has been studied so far, and the study, both theoretical and experimental, resulted in a crude approximation only.[17] Because the theory is inexact, only the final equation which seems to agree with the experimental data is inserted here. It is

$$t_m = \kappa \frac{\eta w^2 E \delta^3}{W_1^2 y_0} ; \tag{49}$$

t_m is time of separation, that is the time interval between the application of weights W, Fig. 35, and the fall of the ribbon. As before, η is viscosity of the liquid adhesive, w the width of the ribbon (normal to the plane of the paper), E is the modulus of elasticity of the ribbon material, δ the thickness of the ribbon, W_1 weight applied to each end (corrected as explained below), and y_0 the initial thickness of the liquid film. The value of κ, although it can be accounted for by theory, is best considered as an empirical constant.

The mechanism for which equation (49) was derived is fully analogous to that of §31. As soon as weights W are applied, underpressure is established in the adhesive and liquid starts to flow toward the median line of the system (this line is parallel to

width w, i.e., normal to the plane of the sketch). The main difference between this and the effect studied by Stefan is that in
the latter case liquid maintains its cylindrical shape, only the
height of the cylinder increasing during the experiment, while
in peeling the shape of the liquid body continues to change from
the first to the last moment of the experiment.

Two additional effects take place in actual stripping experiments. (a) Liquid flows not only from the two ends of the
ribbon toward the median line but also from the two edges of
the ribbon (which are parallel to the length of the latter) toward
the centroid line (which is parallel to and equidistant from the
edges) of the adhesive film. (b) Because menisci (M in Fig. 35)
exist near the two ends of the ribbon, the pressure in the liquid
is less than the atmospheric not only in consequence of the
weights attached but also as a result of capillary pressure which,
for a well wetting liquid, would be about $-2\gamma/y_0$ in the beginning of the experiment but less important afterward; as before,
γ is surface tension. It is difficult to improve the theory by considering these two effects, but apparently they can be corrected
for in the following manner. When the experimental values of
$(1/t_m)$ are plotted as a function of W^2, a straight line is obtained
which crosses the abscissa (i.e., the coordinate of W^2) at a value
which we may denote by W_0^2. Then, W_1 in equation (49) is
simply $W - W_0$.

Constant κ (a pure number) was about 0.2 in the experiments
of reference 17, in which the ribbon was of aluminum, steel, or
copper (0.005 to 0.008 cm. thick) and hydrocarbon polymers
(with viscosities of 75 and 300 g./cm.sec.) were used as tacky
adhesives.

In these experiments the angle of peeling was indefinite.
In several instruments designed for tack measurement, this
angle was kept constant and force required for stripping proved
to depend on this angle. For a definition of the latter and a discussion of its importance see §81.

§37. AN IMPORTANT REASON for the deviation of experimental detachment times from the values predicted by equation
(34) has not been mentioned in §31 because it was not as "scien-

tific" as the others were. This reason is absence of symmetry in the experimental arrangement.

If, for instance, the two plates of Fig. 27 are not parallel, time t is smaller than calculated from their *average* mutual distance because, in liquid flow, the importance of a channel increases more rapidly than in linear manner with the diameter of the channel. Imagine a set of n parallel slits of equal width and of thicknesses δ_1, δ_2, $\cdots$ δ_n. The average thickness would be $\delta_{av} = (1/n)(\delta_1 + \delta_2 + \cdots \delta_n)$ but the volume V of liquid moving through the set would be proportional, see equation (6), §22, to $(\delta_1^3 + \delta_2^3 + \cdots + \delta_n^3)$; thus the contribution of narrow slits is less important for V than for δ_{av}. When the clearance between two discs was 5 microns at one end of a diameter and 23 microns at the opposite end (5 cm. away), the t was about one-third of what it should be[9]. If one of the plates is flat and the other concave, convex or, generally, wavy, see §6, the asymmetry would be as damaging as when the plates are both flat but not mutually parallel.

Similar effects presumably would be observed if, instead of the clearance, the plates themselves would have no cylindrical symmetry; if, say, the bottom plate of Fig. 27 had the shape outlined in Fig. 36 instead of being circular An analogous phenomenon, due to accidental asymmetry, was noticed when an instrument depicted in Fig. 37 was used.[18] This is simply a glass tube partly

FIG. 36. An asymmetrical plate.

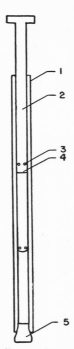

FIG. 37. A penetroviscometer. From reference 18.

filled with an adhesive, into which a coaxial metal rod slowly sinks under its own weight; from the rate of descent the viscosity (or consistency) of the adhesive can be calculated. When, after the descent, the instrument is turned upside down and the rate of emersion of the rod is measured, the experiment is a determination of the tackiness of the adhesive in a tubular lap joint. In a perfectly symmetrical system the two rates (in and out) would be identical. In reality[19] the rod falls out more rapidly than it penetrated into the adhesive. Figure 38 shows the reason of the discrepancy. When the adhesive-air surface is not flat, the distance between the region of atmospheric pressure and that of the underpressure above the inverted rod is not identical around the rod; the Δz of §22 is smaller at the indentation indicated in Fig. 38 than elsewhere. Consequently, $\Delta P/\Delta z$ is greater

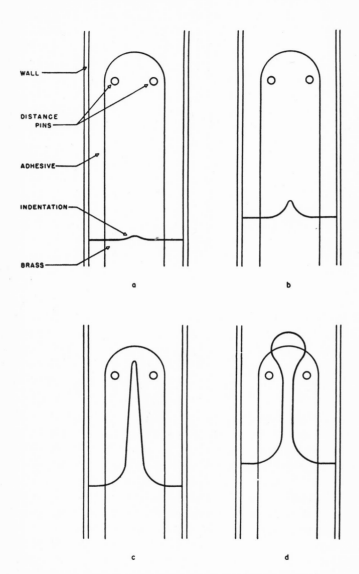

FIG. 38. Effect of asymmetry on time of separation (or tackiness). From reference 19.

at the indentation than in other points; hence, the inward flow
is more rapid here than elsewhere and the indentation gets
deeper. This even more accentuates the difference between Δz
at the indentation and far from it; thus the effect is self-ac-
celerating.

§38.   MANY INSTRUMENTS have been suggested for measuring
tack. Two essential stages are present in each of these measurements, namely (a) making contact and (b) breaking contact.

The method of establishing contact often is selected to be
similar to that in the actual use. Thus, an adhesive tape may be
allowed to settle on a solid under its own weight, if it is intended
for an application excluding an external pressure.[20] If the adhesive is supposed to be called into action after t seconds, also
in the test it is kept in contact with the adherend for t seconds
before detachment is attempted. The requirement of a minimum
tack after t seconds is quite common. Suppose, for instance, that
we have to bend a sheet of paper and to glue the ends together.
The stress produced in the sheet by the bending will tend to
open the seam; thus, an outside force is needed to prevent un-
bending until tackiness is strong enough to overcome the tendency
to unbend; and production is speeded up when this force is applied for a shorter time. This problem arises, for instance, in the
glueing of the flaps of cardboard boxes, see §53. Presumably,
time needed for air to escape greatly influences test results, but
this idea has not yet been considered by experimenters.

In another test for adhesive tapes (ASTM D 1000–53 T),
the tape is placed on a steel plate and a roller of standard shape
and weight is twice passes over the backing of the tape at a
prescribed speed; presumably further rolling would not markedly
enhance the tackiness.

An example in which "autohesion,"[21] i.e., the adherence established on contact of two identical materials, was determined
may be mentioned here. A roller covered with synthetic rubber
was pressed into a plate of the same rubber for a definite time
by a definite force, after which the force needed for separation
was measured.[22] Similar devices have been constructed and tested
later.[1, 2, 23]

In the above instances, the properties of the tacky adhesive were relatively independent of time so that the age of the adhesive material was not critical. A more sensitive system is present in the common gummed tape which is not tacky when dry, becomes tacky when moistened, and ceases to be tacky when moisture evaporates. Evidently, the rheology of this substance in its tacky state varies from second to second. In ASTM test D 773–47, see Fig. 39, moisture is applied with a stand-

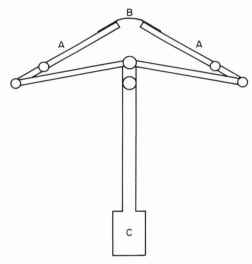

FIG. 39. Tack tester of the type of ASTM D 773–47. From reference 25.

ardized brush and the resistance to separation is measured after a standardized lapse of time; and apparently this degree of standardization is satisfactory for industrial testing.

§39.   As FAR AS breaking the contact is concerned, the majority of the methods may be classified as follows.

1. Determination of the force needed
    1.1 in butt joints
    1.2 in lap joints
    1.3 by peeling
    1.31 at 90°

1.32 at 180°
1.4 in more complex arrangements

2. Determination of the work needed
   2.1 by a swinging pendulum
   2.2 by a rolling cylinder

A scheme of the butt joint is shown in Fig. 27. Instruments of this type have been used by Stefan himself and many times since. Types for routine testing are described, for instance, in references 5 and 8.

The apparatus depicted in Fig. 37, when turned upside down, is an example of tubular lap joint.

Among the many devices suggested for the determination of peeling strength, those in which the angle of peeling (§81) is maintained constant are more likely to afford reproducible results. In the machine outlined in Fig. 40[24] this angle is 90°.

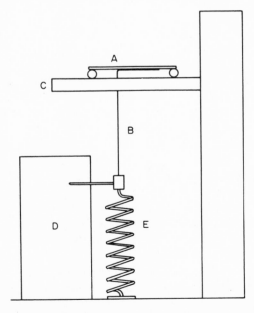

Fig. 40. Tack tester by Orlov.[24] From reference 25.

Ribbon *B* is glued to rigid plate *A* which is mounted on a cart which can roll along the horizontal beam *C* practically without friction. When *C* is gradually lifted, *B* causes an extension of the calibrated spring *E*, and this extension is recorded on drum *D*. As there is no friction, *B* is always perpendicular to *A*.

Peeling at 180° is carried out in several arrangements such as that recommended in the ASTM test D 1000–53 T. The essential features of the instrument are shown in Fig. 41. In it

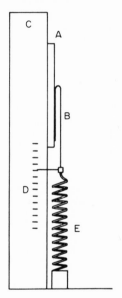

FIG. 41. Tack tester of the ASTM D 1000-53T type. From reference 25.

again *A* is a rigid plate, *B* a flexible ribbon, *D* a scale, and *E* a calibrated spring, while *C* is a stand. In other variants the force is measured by the inclination of a heavy pendulum rather than by the extension of a spring.

An arrangement,[22] which mechanically is as simple as the foregoing devices but would offer considerable obstacles to a theoretical treatment, is illustrated in Fig. 42. Here a lying cylinder (*C*) is being lifted from a plate (*B*) in the direction nor-

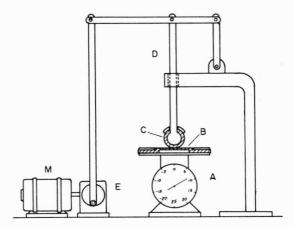

Fig. 42. Tack tester by Busse *et al.*[22]

mal to the plate. The force with which C lifts B is read on the dial of the spring scale A. The rate of movement of C is determined by the speed of motor M and the geometry of the transmitting members D and E.

A machine named *inkometer* was devised to measure the tack of printing inks spread on rollers. Only the principle of its essential part is indicated[25] in Fig. 43. The adhesive is spread over

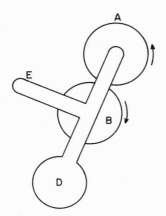

Fig. 43. The essential part of an "inkometer." From reference 25.

drum A kept in rotation by a motor. The "friction" between drums A and B causes a tilt of the pendulum-like system consisting of a bar to which drums B and D and side-arm E are firmly attached. A load is suspended on E to restore the initial position of the bar; the value of this load is a measure of the tack of the adhesive.

When work, rather than force, of separation is to be measured, a pendulum is a suitable device. For instance, the bottom of a freely swinging pendulum is pressed against a vertical plate coated with the tacky material. The plate is h_0 cm. above the lowest position of the pendulum. When the pendulum is released, it does not rise h_0 high on its upswing but only, say, h_1 cm. high. If F is the weight of the pendulum, the work done against the tack of the adhesive is simply $F(h_0 - h_1)$. This method has been employed, for instance, in reference 26.

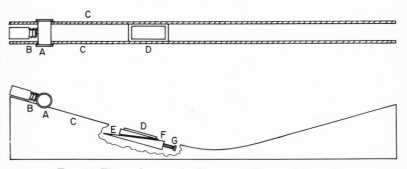

Fig. 44. The tack tester by Voet *et al.* From reference 27.

Figure 44 is a diagram of an apparatus[27] consisting of two bent rails (C) over which a cylinder (A) can roll down (from the release device B) and up the opposite slope. On its downward path the roller passes an inked plate D, loses some of its momentum because of the tackiness of the printing ink, and therefore reaches, in its subsequent ascent, a point (h_1) which is lower than point h_0 from which it started. Letters E, F, and G indicate members serving to adjust the height of the inked plate relative to the rails. The work against tack again is $F(h_0 - h_1)$

and the "specific work" is $F(h_0 - h_1)/A$, A being the area of the plate and F weight of the roller. It is interesting that this specific work increases with the depth of the ink layer but manifests no definite correlation with the viscosity (or consistency) of the ink. Apparently, the greater the viscosity η, the more shallow is the layer disturbed by the rolling cylinder but at the same time the work required to achieve a given disturbance is greater the greater η. A theory of the resistance to rolling a cylinder along a surface covered with a viscoplastic substance has been published by Kotova.[28]

REFERENCES

1. Beaven, E. W. J., Croft-White, P. G., Garner, P. J., and Rooney, G., *Proc. 2nd Rubber Technol. Conf., London* **1948**, p. 224 (1948).
2. Beckwith, R. K., Welch, L. M., Nelson, J. F., Chaney, A. L., and McCracken, E. A., *Ind. Eng. Chem.* **41**, 2247 (1949).
3. Voyutskii, S. S., and Zamazii, V. M., *Doklady Akad. Nauk S.S.S.R.* **81**, 63 (1951).
4. Forbes, W. G., and McLeod, L. A., *Trans. Inst. Rubber Ind.* **34**, 154 (1958).
5. Wetzel, F. H., *Am. Soc. Testing Materials Bull. No.* **221**, 64 (1957).
6. Stefan, J., *Sitzber. Akad. Wiss. Wien, Math.-naturw. Kl.* **69**, 713 (1874).
7. Ormandy, E., *Engineer* **143**, 362, 393 (1927).
8. Green, H., *Ind. Eng. Chem., Anal. Ed.* **13**, 632 (1941).
9. Bikerman, J. J., *Trans. Soc. Rheology* **1**, 3 (1957).
10. Banks, W. H., and Mill, C. C., *J. Colloid Sci.* **8**, 137 (1953).
11. Strasburger, H., *J. Colloid Sci.* **13**, 218 (1958).
12. Heidebroek, E., *Ber. Verhandl. sächs. Akad. Wiss. Leipzig, Math.-naturw. Kl.* **97**, No. 6, 20 (1952).
13. Bikerman, J. J., *J. Soc. Chem. Ind.* **62**, 41 (1943).
14. Fuks, G. I., *Doklady Akad. Nauk S.S.S.R.* **113**, 635 (1957).
15. Needs, S. J., *Trans. Am. Soc. Mech. Engrs.* **62**, 331 (1940).
16. Scott, J. R., *Trans. Inst. Rubber Ind.* **7**, 169 (1931).
16a. Dahlquist, C. A., *Adhesives Age* **2**, No. 10, 25 (1959).
17. Bikerman, J. J., and Yap, W., *Trans. Soc. Rheology* **2**, 9 (1958).
18. Bikerman, J. J., *J. Colloid Sci.* **3**, 75 (1948).
19. Bikerman, J. J., *J. Colloid Sci.* **2**, 163 (1947).
20. Chang, F. S. C., *Rubber Chem. and Technol.* **30**, 847 (1957).
21. Zhukov, I. I., and Talmud, S. L., *J. Rubber Ind. (U.S.S.R.)* **12**, 1005 (1935); *Chem. Abstr.* **30**, 6982 (1936).

22. Busse, W. F., Lambert, J. M., and Verdery, R. B., *J. Appl. Phys.* **17**, 336 (1946).
23. Pickup, B., *Trans. Inst. Rubber Ind.* **33**, 58 (1957).
24. Orlov, A. I., *Zavodskaya Lab.* **7**, 977 (1938).
25. Bikerman, J. J., A review of adhesion tests. *Patra Packaging Bull. No.* **2**, (1945).
26. Deryagin, B. V., and Sorokin, S. M., *in* "Physico-chemical Fundamentals of Printing Processes," p. 207. Moscow, 1937.
27. Voet, A., and Geffken, C. F., *Ind. Eng. Chem.* **43**, 1614 (1951).
28. Kotova, L. I., *Zhur. Tekh. Fiz.* **27**, 1540 (1957).

CHAPTER 5

Setting

§40. As mentioned in §15, some commercial adhesives are permanently tacky but the majority of glues lose their tack and become definitely solid soon after application. This phenomenon is called setting. According to the mechanism of their setting, the customary adhesives can be classified in three main groups, which set as a result of cooling, of solvent removal, or of a chemical reaction, respectively.

Many substances of those that can be molten by heating and solidified by cooling can act as adhesives.[1] Apparently there is another more or less necessary condition. If the rate of nucleation is great compared with the rate of crystal growth, the adhesive film after setting is more likely to be continuous and therefore strong than when the crystal growth is rapid, the nucleation is slow, and the large crystals formed may be separated by voids or greatly contaminated regions. Polymers usually do not form separate crystals on cooling; thus, they make good adhesives if they do not decompose before melting. Polyethylene, polystyrene, poly(vinyl acetate), and other thermoplastic high-molecular substances were successfully used for making adhesive joints in this manner; see, for instance, references 2, 3, 4, 5.

Heat-sealing often used in industry is essentially the same process. Asphalts (bitumens) usually are liquid when brought in contact with sand, masonry, and so on and solidify on cooling. Solders are perhaps the most important adhesives applied in the molten state; their properties which cannot be discussed here have been reviewed, for instance, in reference 6. Animal glue often is applied hot ("molten") and rapidly sets on cooling, but evaporation of the solvent (that is, water) also contributes to the setting.

Solvent removal is the main or the sole process by which, probably, the majority of commercial, especially the household, adhesives solidify. These are sometimes denoted as solvent cements. It may be asked: what properties must a solid A, a solvent B, and solutions of A in B possess for these solutions to be usable as cements? Apparently no answer to this question is available in the literature. Presumably here again formation of separate crystals is the danger to be avoided. Thus, aqueous solution of sodium chloride is not an adhesive because the salt crystallizes out as separate cubes. If the solution during its evaporation becomes very viscous before crystallization starts, the danger has almost passed as high viscosity depresses crystal growth.

Solvent can be removed not only by evaporation but also by imbibition by porous adsorbents such as wood or paper. The separation of solute and solvent by filter paper is a well-known phenomenon; a successful method of analysis ("capillary analysis") is based on it; see, e.g., reference 7. However, solutions generally subjected to this treatment contain dyes or compounds of biological importance; no publication reporting a scientific study of the fractionation of an adhesive liquid into its components by imbibition came to the author's notice.

It is clear that solvent cements can be used only as long as at least one of the two adherends is porous (or otherwise permeable for the solvent). The evaporation of solvent from a narrow space between two nonporous solids (such as metals or glasses) would take too long; sometimes it is not completed several months after the preparation of the adhint.

Some of the oldest and the newest adhesives belong to the third group, that which sets because of a chemical reaction. The venerable plaster of Paris is a well-known example: calcium sulfate hemihydrate is mixed with water, reacts with it, and forms an agglomeration of calcium sulfate dihydrate crystals, strong enough for many purposes. The reactions causing the hardening of portland cement are similar but, in spite of its name, portland cement probably would not qualify as an adhesive.

Organic reactions resulting in setting of adhesives, as a rule, are polymerization or addition or condensation phenomena. In the first type two identical or nearly identical molecules unite, and in the second type the two combining molecules are quite different, but in both cases no other product results except the double molecule. In the third type, water or another small molecule forms as a by-product.

Cross-linking of two polymer esters of maleic acid and ethylene glycol is an example of the first type:

$$
\begin{array}{llll}
-O-CH_2-CH_2-O-CO-CH & & HC-CO-O-CH_2-CH_2-O- \\
& \parallel & + & \parallel & = \\
-O-CH_2-CH_2-O-CO-CH & & HC-CO-O-CH_2-CH_2-O-
\end{array}
$$

$$
\begin{array}{l}
-O-CH_2-CH_2-O-CO-CH-CH-CO-O-CH_2-CH_2-O- \\
\qquad\qquad\qquad\qquad\quad | \quad\ | \\
-O-CH_2-CH_2-O-CO-CH-CH-CO-O-CH_2-CH_2-O-
\end{array}
$$

Setting of epoxy resins illustrates the chemistry of addition reactions:

Curing of a phenol-formaldehyde resin is a typical condensation process:

More about these reactions can be found in books on adhesives (as distinct from this monograph dealing with adhints), e.g., in reference 8.

High molecular compounds produced by polymerization or addition can, and those yielded by condensation usually cannot, be applied as adhesives between nonporous adherends. If a condensation polymer must serve as an adhesive between two continuous surfaces, the major part of water (afforded by condensation) is removed before the adherends are pressed together.

§41.   IF SOLIDIFICATION of adhesives occurred without any associated change, that is if their viscosity and yield stress increased during setting while all other physical and chemical properties remained unaltered, both study and use of adhints would have been greatly simplified. Of the numberless changes accompanying the setting of adhesives, those that lower the final strength of adhints (see §15) may, for convenience, be classified in five divisions:

1. physical changes resulting in weak boundary layers (§15)

2. physical changes resulting in unfavorable stress concentrations,

3. physico-chemical changes resulting in weak boundary layers,

4. chemical changes resulting in weak boundary layers, and

5. formation of weak spots in the bulk of the adhesive film.

Physical Formation of Weak Boundary Layers

§42.   1. THAT PHYSICAL CHANGE which most readily gives rise to weak boundary layers is contraction associated with setting. The amount of this contraction is greatest for adhesives applied as solutions (§40). These usually contain 20 to 60 weight per cents of solids which, on the average, would be equivalent to 15 to 50 volume per cents. This means that a liquid adhesive completely filling the space between two rigid adherends would fill only 15 to 50% of the space after solidification, thus leaving up to 85% voids. Evidently a system thus constructed would not be strong.

The contraction associated with the other two classes of adhesives is smaller but still can be dangerous. The volume of solid adhesive at room temperature divided by its volume above the softening and melting range is, or would be, for instance, for polyethylenes: 0.86[9], 0.80[10] and for polystyrenes: about 0.95.[9,11]

The polymerization, addition, and condensation processes of the third class cause similar shrinkages. Thus a unit volume of a liquid polyester may result in a volume of 0.90, and a liquid volume of an epoxy resin may give a volume of 0.95–0.97 after setting.[12]

In industry, some adhesives are classified as sealers. The shrinkage of some of these materials is very small but a volume contraction of about 4% seems to be more common, and some sealers shrink by as much as 18%. Nevertheless, they can be successfully used to fill clearances of predetermined dimensions. Apparently, stress concentrations caused by shrinkage, §43, are small in typical sealers because these are still relatively mobile when the main contraction takes place.

Some inorganic substances are exceptionally good, as far as shrinkage is concerned, since they expand during freezing. The volume increase observed in the transformation water → ice presumably is an important reason for the unexpected adherence of ice to every kind of solid including those not wetted by water.[13] Suppose that liquid water is forced into a depression on a poorly wettable surface, as indicated in Fig. 45 similar to Fig. 10 in §14.

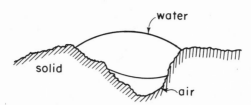

FIG. 45. Mechanical attachment of ice to a rough surface.

When the drop solidifies, it expands, pushes the hills apart, and is gripped by them, analogously to the snap fastener effect of §14. However, no experiments on which this explanation could be tested are known to the author.

Solders containing bismuth and/or antimony expand on solidification in some range of composition. Thus, many alloys containing lead, tin, antimony, cadmium, and indium increase in volume during the liquid → solid transformation as long as bismuth content is 55% or greater;[14] when this content is 48–55% there is no measurable volume change on freezing.

Shrinkage of many adhesives can be reduced by mixing the liquid adhesive with a solid powder whose volume remains almost constant during setting. If, for instance, the volume percentage of this powder (usually denoted by the term *filler*) is $x\%$ and the relative shrinkage of pure adhesive is $y\%$, then the relative shrinkage of the filled adhesive is approximately $(1 - x)y\%$.

The common way of avoiding coarsely porous adhints is to maintain a constant pressure on the assembly during the main part of its solidification process and to eliminate anything that can prevent gradual coming together of the adherends during the rest of the setting time. If this is not done, the final strength of an adhint usually is impaired. If the clearance between two solids is filled with a liquid adhesive and the dimensions of the former are kept constant while the latter sets, the breaking stress of the joint (as a rule) first increases (because of increase in viscosity or consistency), reaches a maximum, and then decreases (because of void formation).[15]

When void formation is not completely averted, its deleterious effect on the strength of an adhint depends both on the shape and size of the void and on its position. Stress concentration around voids is discussed in §§62 to 64. Here the position of the bubbles is considered. As no deliberate experiments concerning the matter are known to the author, only general and tentative statements are possible.

As a rule, a bubble is more dangerous when it is situated near the 3-phase line, see for instance §43, less dangerous when it clings to the adherend-adhesive boundary far from the air phase, and relatively innocuous when it is surrounded by the adhesive; in Fig. 46 the weakening effect decreases from *a* to *b* to *c*. The

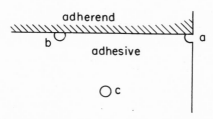

Fig. 46. The weakening effect of a bubble is greatest in position *a* and least in position *c*.

next question, namely what conditions of setting give rise preferentially to bubbles in *a*, *b*, or *c* position, also can be answered in very general terms only. It is known that *growth* of a solid (from a melt below the freezing temperature or from a supersaturated solution) is easier than *start* of a new crystal or a disconnected chunk of amorphous solid. Thus, when an adhesive film sets, there will be a tendency for the solid phase to concentrate around the regions in which nucleation started and for the voids to be as far from these regions as possible.

From this point of view, adhesives fall again in the same three classes as mentioned in §40. Those that set by cooling will have their voids in the region which cooled last. Usually, this means the center of the adhesive film. Only when the heat conductance of the adherends is considerably less than that of the adhesive, bubbles of the *b* type would be most probable. Solvent cements lose their solvent to the atmosphere and, consequently, also start solidifying around the periphery of the adhint. However, voids in position *b* are more likely in this than in the preceding class because diffusion of the solvent from the bottom of a narrow crack such as illustrated in Fig. 26, is a relatively slow process; the adhesive just outside the crack will set before that in the crack and, finally, there will be a bubble of solvent vapor in the depth of the crack. In the third class, the rate of solidification, at least as a first approximation, is identical over the adhesive film and no position of a bubble is more probable than any other.

Hardly any experimental proof exists for the conclusions arrived at in the preceding paragraph. If these conclusions are correct, then the most dangerous voids (position *a*) form not because of the preferred direction of crystal growth but because of shrinkage stresses, §43.

The higher probability of voids in the regions of latest solidification may supply a satisfactory explanation for the observation which was believed[16] to prove the existence of "specific adhesion." When animal glue is poured on wood, it is seen that the liquid fills the pores of the solid. After the setting, solid glue usually is visible as a coating on the internal pore walls. It may be asked why the solid does not remain as a bar or a blob somewhere in the middle of the pore. The answer given in earlier times was that pore walls "specifically attracted" the glue. An answer which at present appears more convincing is based on the rule that solidification tends to proceed around the first nuclei. If the pressure of water vapor above the wood in the state it was used for glueing was smaller than that of the glue solution, the solution lost its water to the wood, solidification of the glue started at the wood surface, and a glue coat remained on the pore walls after complete removal of water.

Shrinkage is not the only physical change which may cause formation of weak boundary layers. If the adhesive is a suspension, it has a tendency to settle and the upper adherend may be in contact with a more dilute suspension than the bottom member. This effect is said to be important for the adherence of portland cement to metal bars used for reinforcing.[17]

Frozen Stresses

§43. 2. THE VALUES for shrinkage recorded in §42 are valid only as long as the solid in its final state is stress-free, that is as long as the contraction was not restrained by external forces. Consider an adhesive filling the clearance, of constant thickness h_0, between two parallel plates. If the adhesive were permitted to set in the absence of external restraints, its thickness would have been, say, h_1. As long as $(h_0 - h_1)/h_0$ is smaller than the total relative elongation of the adhesive, this will not break (except, perhaps, near the 3-phase line defined in §17). Far from the edge of the adhint, i.e., in the region where the strain is normal to the adherend plates, the stress "frozen" in the adhesive film is $E_2(h_0 - h_1)/h_0$, assuming that the adhesive follows Hooke's law with a modulus of elasticity E_2. No void will form as long as this quantity is less than the ultimate tensile strength of the adhesive, but the external stress required to break the adhint (in the adhesive film) will be correspondingly smaller. Let the tensile strength of the stress-free adhesive (still treated as a Hookean solid) be f_m; then only a tensile stress

$$f = f_m - \frac{E_2(h_0 - h_1)}{h_0} \tag{50}$$

would be needed for rupturing the prestressed material. Also equation (50) seems never to have been tested; in any eventual testing the stress concentrations near the 3-phase lines should be avoided as much as possible.

Stresses at the 3-phase line were first calculated for glass-to-metal seals because for this combination the volume changes on cooling and heating are more dangerous than for any of the usual adhints;[18] the total relative elongation of massive glass is so small (near 0.5%) that $(h_0 - h_1)/h_0$ achieved by even moderate temperature difference may exceed it. However, the equations obtained should be applicable to any adherend-adhesive combination.

Butt joints will be considered first.[19, 20, 21] The calculation has been carried out[22, 23] for two thin-walled hollow cylinders stuck together with their annular ends in contact. If R is the external and $R - \delta$ is the internal radius of the hollow cylinder, the equations contain the product $R\delta$; apparently, when two plates $l \times w \times h_1$ and $l \times w \times h_2$ are in contact along the area $l \times w$, these equations are approximately valid also for the central parts of the lengths l and w, far from the corners, if 0.5 w and 0.5 l, respectively, is substituted for $(R\delta)^{0.5}$.

In Fig. 47 the upper half represents the adherend and the lower, the adhesive, both as hollow cylinders. Air is at the right of the sketch. If the two bodies did not deform each other, their outlines would be straight right to the x axis. In reality, the transition from the external radius $R + x_1$ of the adherend to the external radius $R - x_2$ of the adhesive is gradual as shown by the continuous line; x_1 and x_2 exist because the cylinders were joined at a high temperature and had, at this temperature, identical radii; during cooling they contracted to different extents.

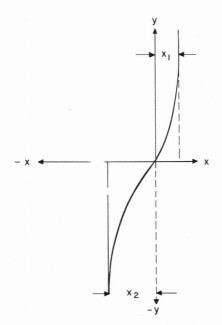

Fig. 47. Shrinkage stress at the boundary of two hollow cylinders.

R is the radius of the 3-phase line. Let the intercept of this line with the plane of the drawing be the origin of the coordinate system. Thus, at $y > 0$, the value of $x_1 - x$ is the deviation of the adherend-air surface from the unstressed position; analogously, $x - x_2$ is the deformation suffered by the adhesive (at $y < 0$).

The equation of the adherend-air boundary is

$$x_1 - x = (e^{-\beta_1 y}/2\beta_1{}^3 D_1)[P \cos \beta_1 y - \beta_1 M(\cos \beta_1 y - \sin \beta_1 y)] \tag{51a}$$

and of the adhesive-air boundary

$$x_2 - x = (e^{-\beta_2 y}/2\beta_2^3 D_2)[P \cos \beta_2 y + \beta_2 M(\cos \beta_2 y - \sin \beta_2 y)]. \tag{51b}$$

In these equations,

$$\beta_1 = [3(1 - \nu_1{}^2)/R^2 \delta^2]^{0.25}$$
$$\beta_2 = [3(1 - \nu_2{}^2)/R^2 \delta^2]^{0.25}$$
$$D_1 = E_1 \delta^3/12(1 - \nu_1{}^2)$$
$$D_2 = E_2 \delta^3/12(1 - \nu_2{}^2).$$

P is the tension (g./sec.²) acting along the 3-phase line toward the axis of the cylinder in the adherend and away from this axis in the adhesive, and M is the bending moment at the 3-phase line. E_1 and E_2 are the moduli of elasticity, and ν_1 and ν_2 the Poisson ratios of the two materials.

The value of $R + x_1$ may be considered to be unaffected by the shrinkage of the adhesive. If the relative linear contraction (which is about one-third of the volume shrinkage for which numerical data were listed in §42) of the adhesive is λ (or $100\,\lambda\%$), then $R - x_2 = (1 - \lambda)(R + x_1)$ and $x_1 + x_2 = \lambda R + \lambda x_1$ or, approximately,

$$x_1 + x_2 = \lambda R. \tag{52}$$

Also, because no discontinuity is expected when the sign of y values changes from positive to negative, dy/dx must be identical at $y = 0$ for both adherend-air and adhesive-air boundaries.

These two conditions are sufficient to calculate P and M as functions of λR, β_1, β_2, D_1, and D_2; thus,

$$P = \frac{4\beta_1^3\beta_2^3 D_1 D_2 (\beta_1 D_1 + \beta_2 D_2)\lambda R}{\beta_1^4 D_1^2 + 2\beta_1\beta_2(\beta_1^2 + \beta_1\beta_2 + \beta_2^2)D_1 D_2 + \beta_2^4 D_2^2} \quad (53)$$

and

$$M = \frac{2\beta_1\beta_2 D_1 D_2 (\beta_1^2 D_1 - \beta_2^2 D_2)\lambda R}{\beta_1^4 D_1^2 + 2\beta_1\beta_2(\beta_1^2 + \beta_1\beta_2 + \beta_2^2)D_1 D_2 + \beta_2^4 D_2^2} \quad (54)$$

As β_1 and β_2 usually will be very similar, we may set each of them equal to a quantity β; thus

$$P = \frac{4\beta^3 D_1 D_2 (D_1 + D_2)\lambda R}{D_1^2 + 6D_1 D_2 + D_2^2} \quad (55)$$

is obtained. Often, D_2 will be small compared with D_1; in these instances

$$P = \frac{4\beta^3 D_1 D_2 \lambda R}{D_1 + 6D_2} \quad (56)$$

and

$$M = \frac{2D_1 D_2 \lambda R}{D_1 + 6D_2} \quad (57)$$

Theoretically, P acts on the 3-phase line which, like any other geometrical line, is infinitely thin; thus the stress caused by P is infinitely large. Actually, the "line" will have a thickness determined by surface roughness, see §§3 and 67.2.

An equation was given for the case of two very long plates, of width w, glued together and subjected to a medium in which the upper plate does, and the lower does not swell.[24] The mathematics ought to be identical also when the adhint cools and the contraction of the lower plate is greater than that of the upper member. If after cooling the width of the latter, see Fig. 48, is $w + \epsilon_0 w$, the maximum shear stress along the x axis near point m is approximately

$$\tau = 0.7\ \epsilon_0 (E_x G_{xy})^{0.5} \quad (58)$$

E_x being the common modulus of elasticity of the two members

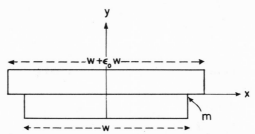

FIG. 48. Shrinkage stress in two plates glued together.

in the x direction and G_{xy} being the modulus of shear in the xy plane.

§44.   THE TOPOGRAPHY of shrinkage stresses in a butt joint was expressed as a series and compared with photoelasticity results on polymer plates.[25, 26] As equations (51) show, the strain and consequently the stress in the adherend and the adhesive vary periodically (as a sum of sine and cosine terms) when the distance from the adherend-adhesive interface increases. This periodicity was detected[27] in glass on which a gelatin film was formed by depositing an aqueous gelatin solution and permitting water to evaporate. The results are exemplified by Fig. 49. Its ordinate represents the stress in glass determined from the birefringence, and the abscissa is the distance from the glass-gelatin interface. Contrary to what we would expect if we had no theory, stress intensity does not simply decay the further we move away from the surface; on the contrary, stress becomes negative (in the instance of Fig. 49 this happened in about 0.3 cm. from the interface), then again zero and, presumably, would be found positive at even greater distances. In this system, positive stress means compressing glass by gelatin.

Extrapolation of the curve of Fig. 49 to zero distance leads to a value of about 180 kg.wt./cm.^{2} ($\approx$2500 psi or 1.8×10^8 baryes) for the stress along the interface. This maximum value σ_m of the "frozen stress" was studied[27] as a function of time (that is, during the setting of the film) and of the dimensions of the film. Figure 50 shows that σ_m is a linear function of the film thickness h_0 when this varies between 0.005 and 0.020 cm.

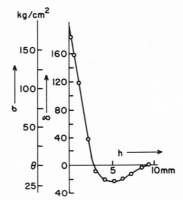

FIG. 49. Shrinkage stress in glass on which a gelatin film has dried. Abscissa: distance from glass-gelatin surface, in cm. Ordinate: stress in kg. wt./cm.² (δ is optical path difference.) From reference 27.

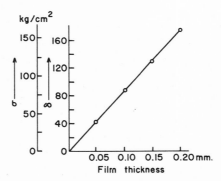

FIG. 50. Shrinkage stress along the glass-gelatin interface, see Fig. 49. Abscissa: gelatin film thickness in cm. Ordinate: stress in kg. wt./cm.² (δ is optical path difference.) From reference 27.

When a gelatin gel was permitted to set between two glass plates, the birefringence in the plates was great near the film-air boundary and small in the center of the plate. See also §46.

Stresses analogous to those depicted in Fig. 49 occur also when an electrodeposit (e.g., nickel plated on a nickel disc) contracts during its recrystallization. For instance, a metal film is electroplated on one side of a flexible metal strip whose one end is fixed in a holder. The strip bends. If Y is the deflection of the free end, δ and h are the thicknesses of strip and deposit, respectively, l_0 is the strip length, and E the modulus of elasticity of the strip material, then the mean stress acting on the strip is (e.g., reference 28)

$$\sigma = 4E\delta^2 Y/3hl_0^2. \tag{59}$$

If this stress is determined at different thicknesses h, and the "instantaneous stress" σ_h calculated[29] from equation

$$\sigma_h = \sigma + h\frac{d\sigma}{dh} \tag{60}$$

is found, σ_h depends on h, i.e., on the distance from the interface, in a manner analogous to the dependence illustrated in Fig. 49. Contrary to the maximum stress plotted in Fig. 50, the average stress σ in the electrodeposit usually is smaller the thicker the film.

§45. THE CASE of tubular lap joints has been discussed many years before that of butt joints. Let an adhesive sleeve of thickness $b-a$ set around a solid adherend cylinder of radius a, see Fig. 51. If the adhesive contracts more than does the adherend, three types of stress will be established in the sleeve, namely p_r along the radius r (r is a variable), p_θ parallel to the circumference of adherend, and p_z parallel to the z axis. If it is assumed that p_z is independent of r and z, that is if the stress concentrations near the 3-phase boundary are disregarded, the three stress systems can be calculated,[30, 31] namely

$$p_r = \frac{E_2\lambda}{1 + \alpha + \alpha\beta(E_2/E_1)}\left(\frac{a^2}{r^2} - \frac{a^2}{b^2}\right), \tag{61}$$

$$p_\theta = -\frac{E_2\lambda}{1 + \alpha + \alpha\beta(E_2/E_1)}\left(\frac{a^2}{b^2} + \frac{a^2}{r^2}\right), \tag{62}$$

and

$$p_z = -\frac{E_2\lambda}{1 + \alpha + \alpha\beta(E_2/E_1)}\left[2\nu\frac{a^2}{b^2} + \frac{1 + \alpha + \alpha\beta(E_2/E_1)}{1 + \beta(E_2/E_1)}\right]. \tag{63}$$

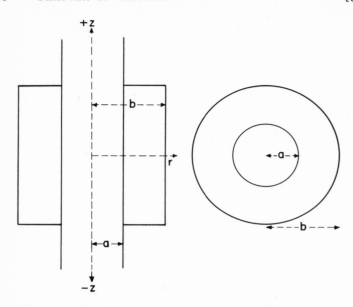

FIG. 51. Shrinkage stress in a cylindrical coating.

Here $\alpha = (a^2/b^2)(2\nu - 1)$, $\beta = (b^2/a^2) - 1$, E_1 and E_2 are the moduli of elasticity of adherend and adhesive, respectively, and λ has the meaning defined in §43. The Poisson ratio ν is assumed to be equal for the two substances.

It is seen that radial stress p_r, as it should, disappears at the adhesive-air interface (that is, at $r = b$); no calculation apparently has been done for real adhints in which the adhesive sleeve is in its turn surrounded with a cylinder of the second adherend. In any case, the greatest p_r occurs at the inner boundary of the adhesive, i.e., at $r = a$. The absolute value of p_θ also is greatest at $r = a$. The three stresses have somewhat similar magnitudes. If we write h for $b - a$ and if h is small compared with a, the greatest radial stress p_r is approximately $2E_2\lambda h/a$. The p_z under these circumstances would not be greatly different from $2E_2\lambda\nu$ or from $E_2\lambda$. A Hookean solid breaks when tensile stress of ϵE_2 is applied to it, ϵ being the total relative elongation. Thus, p_z caused by setting will approximately reach the value of the breaking stress when $\lambda = \epsilon$ and will be nearer the breaking stress the smaller the difference $\epsilon - \lambda$.

§46. THE EQUATIONS of §§43 and 45, which are approximate only because they assume the materials involved to be Hookean solids and use also other inexact postulates, sometimes are difficult to apply insofar as the value of λ is not always definite. This is caused by relaxation effects occurring in the customary adhesives; see the discussion of sealers in §42. Suppose that an unattached film of the adhesive would be l cm. long. As a part of an adhint, it is forced to have the length l_1. Thus, in the joint, it would be under a permanent tensile stress equal to $E_2(l_1 - l_0)/l_0$, if E_2 is Young's modulus of the adhesive. In reality, stress would be smaller than expected, and the difference may be considerable even for materials as viscous as a glass at 425°.[32]

The shrinkage stresses produced in a gelatin membrane solidified in a rigid ring were measured[33] by creating a pressure difference (p) between the two sides of the membrane and measuring the central displacement (z) of the latter.   If the membrane is extremely thin and flexible, the relation between p and z is given simply by

$$\frac{z}{p} = \frac{a^2}{4\Gamma},   \tag{64}$$

Γ being the shrinkage tension, in this connection analogous to surface tension of liquids. Equation (64) is approximately valid also for real membranes if z is very small. In this instance, a simple trigonometric transformation shows that, a being the radius of the membrane, a^2/z is approximately equal to $2R$, if R is the radius of curvature of the distended membrane; thus equation (64) is analogous to equation (2) of capillary pressure. If δ is the thickness of the membrane, shrinkage stress is Γ/δ. Stresses as high as 3×10^8 baryes (or 5000 psi) have been computed in this manner. See also §44.

Apparently, unwanted stresses can form not only because of the setting of the adhesive but also as a result of incorrect handling of the adhint. When two pieces of glass with a liquid adhesive between them were cured at 149°C under a strong pressure, the final strength of the joint showed a maximum when this pressure was 200 psi (14 bars); for the four adhesives studied the strength after heating at 14 bars was by about 10, 10, 10, and 150% greater than when the pressure was 7 bars and about 20% greater than when the pressure was 21 bars.[34] The improvement caused by an increase in pressure might be attributed to the more complete squeezing out of the bubble-containing polymer, see §26, but the decrease in strength observed when pressure rose from 14 to 21 bars must have another explanation. It seems possible that high pressure caused elastic deformation of the glass plates and, in particular, of the microscopic or submicroscopic hills on the glass surfaces in contact with the adhesive; when pressure was released, the plates and the hills tended to regain their initial shape and thus caused stresses unsuspected by the experimenter.

Weak Boundary Layers of Physico-Chemical Origin

§47. 3. Between predominantly physical and predominantly chemical phenomena occurring in the setting of adhesives, we may place physico-chemical effects. Mutual dissolution of adherend and adhesive is an example of the latter class.

Iron is markedly soluble in molten copper but these metals are almost immiscible in solid state. When copper was used as an adhesive ("brazing compound") between two bars of mild steel, some dissolution of iron in liquid copper took place. On cooling, iron dendrites precipitated in the adhesive film (of copper).[35] In this instance, crystal separation caused no weakening of the interfacial layer, but it is clear that an analogous crystallization may give rise to weak spots in another system. Metallographic examination of welded joints has been performed many times but its results are not reviewed in this book.

The following observation[36, 37] seems to indicate another possible source of weakness in some interfaces between copper and other metals. When a plate of copper coated with brass or with a Cu 93, Al 7% alloy was heated, e.g., for 25 days at 800°

and the interface then examined, numerous holes of, e.g., 0.001 cm. in diameter were seen in the alloy near its boundary with copper. Apparently, zinc or aluminum diffused into copper more rapidly than copper did into the alloy phase, thus leaving voids in the alloy. The atomic reason for this effect seems still to be obscure but, whatever the reason, if something of this kind, on a smaller scale, occurs during soldering or brazing, the porous interfacial layer is likely to be weak.

Interpenetration of the two polymers when one is used as the adherend and the other (in molten or dissolved form) as the adhesive, has been considered many times, see, for instance, references 38, 39, 40, but the dependence of the depth of the mixing zone on external conditions (time, temperature, and so on) and the composition of the polymers appears still to be unknown.

§48. AN IMPORTANT CLASS of weak boundary layers seems to be formed by *syneresis*. Syneresis is separation of a homogeneous liquid solution into a gel and a dilute solution on cooling. Suppose that x parts of a polymer can be dissolved in $100-x$ parts of a plasticizer at the boiling point of the latter. If, now, this saturated solution is permitted to cool, two phases gradually emerge in it; one phase is gel-like and contains almost the whole of the polymer only slightly contaminated with the solvent, while the other phase is frankly liquid and contains only $x_0\%$ of the polymer, x_0 being a small fraction of x. If $100 - x \ll x$, that is the initial amount of the plasticizer is small, the liquid after the cooling does not form a layer above or around the gel but rather remains on the gel blob in the shape of a thin coating.

If the adhesive was applied as a melt and syneresis occurred in it during subsequent solidification, the liquid phase will occupy at least a part of the adhesive-adherend interface, and failure of the joint will take place in the liquid layer at a stress much smaller than would be expected from the strength of uncontaminated adhesive.

Commercial polyethylene (of 1958) is a mixture of substances of different molecular weights and, often, of hydrocarbons and nonhydrocarbons (ketones, etc.). Low-molecular hydrocarbons and oxygenated impurities may be expected to separate from polyethylene polymer with a relative ease and, consequently, be the main constituents of the postulated liquid phase resulting from syneresis. These ingredients were removed from three commercial polyethylenes by dissolving these in toluene (or another hydrocarbon solvent) and precipitating the high-molecular polymer by acetone or butanone. The amounts thus removed apparently did not exceed 1% of the initial material. The mechanical properties, such as modulus of elasticity or ultimate breaking strength, were not significantly altered by the treatment. The contact angles between polyethylene, water, and air were almost identical for commercial and for treated polyethylene wax. If the original sample contained carbonyl groups detectable in the infrared spectrum, the corresponding absorption peaks were absent from the spectrum of the purified material. However, the main difference was that commercial polyethylenes gave very weak joints with every solid tested, while adhints made with the treated polyethylenes were stronger than the adhesive in bulk, see §85. Thus, elimination of the ingredients capable of producing weak boundary layers by syneresis made formation of proper adhints possible.[4, 41]

Several other treatments of commercial polyethylene have been advocated and, apparently, used with some success in industry. They include, e.g., irradiation, rinsing with a chromic acid solution,[42] and flaming. It is believed by many users of these treatments that the latter cause oxidation of the polyethylene surface although an oxidized layer usually cannot be detected by an examination of the infrared absorption spectrum.[43] Presumably, the successful procedures achieve adhesiveness in polyethylenes by a mechanism analogous to that outlined in the preceding paragraph. Superficial attack by acid or flame destroys some of the low-molecular ingredients present in the surface layer; we may expect these ingredients (especially those already oxygenated) to be more reactive than the long-chain polyethylene itself. Thus, syneresis near the surface is avoided. A powerful buttress for this explanation is supplied by the observation[44] that passing a stream of hot nitrogen over a polyethylene plate improves the adhesiveness of the plate about as much as sub-

jecting it to a flame of illuminating gas. It is clear that evaporation of impurities may be as rapid in nitrogen as in the gas mixture present in the flame (depending above all on temperature)
while no significant oxidation would be achieved in a gas almost
free of oxygen.

A trivial source of weak boundary layers was noticed[45] when
mercury was used as the adhesive. If mercury and the adherend
were cooled separately in air before being combined, a loose
layer of hoarfrost formed on their surfaces and precluded formation of strong adhints.

Weak Boundary Layers of Chemical Origin

§49. 4. CHEMICAL CHANGES resulting in weak boundary
layers have been observed in several systems.

When rubber is vulcanized in contact with brass, copper of
the brass reacts with sulfur of the rubber, forming copper sulfides.
The amount of sulfides and the strength of the brass-rubber bond
depend on the brass quality and on the percentage of sulfur in
the rubber. In one series of experiments,[46] a mixture of rubber,
sulfur, and some other ingredients was dissolved in benzene,
spread over a brass surface, and partially cured for 5 to 20
minutes; when the coating was then dissolved in benzene, measurable quantities of sulfur (detectable by chemical analysis)
remained in the solid. The amount of this sulfur, its increase with
duration of curing, and, above all, the form in which the sulfur
compound was present were different for brasses suitable and
those unsuitable for bonding. When the sulfur content of the
mix was 10%, the sulfur compound on the brass surface appeared as a powdery deposit, whatever the properties of the
brass. When only 5% S were present in the mix, the deposit on
poorly bonding brasses was still powdery but was more coherent
on good brass specimens; also the amounts of sulfur bound by
the brass were different; thus, after a curing for 5 minutes,
there was 0.05 mg. S per cm.^{2} of poorly bonding metal and only
0.017 mg./cm.^{2} of suitable alloy. The surface concentration of
sulfur on good brass was only 0.042 mg./cm.^{2} even after 15

min. of curing. Bad brass gave rise to powdery sulfides also when the sulfur concentration in the mix was as low as 2%. The amount of sulfide increased with the duration of curing but the increase was relatively rapid and, apparently, limitless with unsuitable brasses, while with good brasses it was slow and seemed to tend to a limiting value. It appears that small amounts of sulfides are innocuous, perhaps because they do not form separate crystals, while amounts sufficient to give rise to a crystalline layer between brass and rubber ruin the adhesion because a layer of disconnected crystals has a negligible strength, see §40.

The behavior of soldered joints is rather similar. Tin solders on copper or copper alloys form the two intermetallic compounds Cu_3Sn and Cu_6Sn_5 (or $CuSn$). Usually, the amount of Cu_6Sn_5 is much greater than that of Cu_3Sn. The crystals of Cu_6Sn_5 are brittle, and a brittle boundary layer results when their concentration in the interface is significant. Thus[47] the peeling strength of copper-tin-copper joints was about 9×10^6 dynes/cm. width after heating for 1 sec. at 400° and only 2×10^6 dynes/cm. after 30 sec. of heating; and the thickness of the Cu_6Sn_5 interlayer was about 1 micron after 1 sec. and about 6 microns after 30 sec.

§50.   The adherence of copper oxide scale to copper may be hindered by a weak boundary layer. If a wire of particularly pure copper is oxidized in dry air at 900°, it becomes coated with a thin film consisting chiefly of cuprous oxide, with some cupric oxide at the interface with air. This wire can be twisted without losing any of its scale at all temperatures tested above 400°. When an analogous experiment is performed with a wire of copper containing 0.03 to 0.04% phosphorus, a twist causes the wire to shed its coating at both 400 and 500°. This coating contains some cuprous phosphate (Cu_3PO_4). The melt of the phosphate spreads around the grains of Cu_2O and thus, after solidification, produces weak interstitial films between them. The grains are smaller and, consequently, the relative importance of the intergranular weakness is greater, near the metal-oxide interface; hence, rupture may be expected to occur preferentially near this interface, and the flakes to be much greater than single oxide grains; unfortunately, the flake dimensions have not been ascertained by the experimenter.[48]

The adherence of enamel to iron is sensitive to the presence of water during the firing operation. At the high temperatures needed for firing, the reaction $Fe + H_2O \rightarrow FeO + H_2$ occurs, and hydrogen bubbles may afford a weak boundary layer between iron and glass. Water available for this reaction may originate from pickling, washing, and so on, but moisture occluded in the frit (i.e., in the future enamel) was shown[49] in one set of conditions to be more important than any other source. The molten enamel is a well conducting electrolyte, and there must be many local cells on the highly inhomogeneous iron surface. It is believed by some researchers[50] that this electrochemical effect improves adherence. As a metal dissolves at the anodic areas and (probably another) metal is deposited on the cathodic areas, surface roughness of the iron increases; if the adhesion of enamel to iron is a purely mechanical (interlocking) effect, see §14, electrochemical corrosion would help adherence. On the other hand, it is easy to imagine conditions in which corrosion will result in weak boundary layers.

Corrosion may be responsible for the observation often made in industry, that aluminum alloys containing a significant percentage of zinc are more difficult to glue with many polymeric adhesives than aluminum free from zinc.

§51. A WEAK BOUNDARY LAYER can form at the metal-polymer interface if the metal acts as a catalyst for a reaction resulting in a brittle or an oily material. A good example of this behavior was found by Black and Blomquist.[51] If adhints are made between aluminum and aluminum with an experimental adhesive consisting mainly of a phenolic resin (8 parts) and an epoxy resin (1 part), their shear strength at room temperature is near 122 bars (or 1770 psi). Heating the adhints in air at 288° for 100 hours depressed the shear strength (at room temperature) to about 65 bars. If a stainless steel was joined rather than aluminum, the initial strength was not markedly different, but it was lowered to almost zero by the heating as above.

Oxygen was needed for this deterioration of bonds; when heating was performed in nitrogen, only a moderate decrease in strength was noted. Apparently, an ingredient of the steel surface accelerated oxidation of the adhesive by air at 288°. In agreement with this view, the first sign of weakening appeared along the 3-phase line, where the adhesive, the oxidizing agent, and the catalyst met. Presumably, the weak zone grew along the metal surface, where the catalyst concentration was highest, but this point was not recorded.

Table VIII[51] demonstrates the catalytic effect of thin metal

TABLE VIII

EFFECT OF HEATING IN AIR ON ADHINTS BETWEEN DIFFERENT METALS

Metal	Shear strength, bars	
	before heating	after
Aluminum	122	65
Manganese	118	72
Chromium	112	63
Iron	99	38
Nickel	111	47
Zinc	127	78
Copper	96	0
Silver	146	80
Cerium	130	82

films deposited on an aluminum surface by displacement from an acid solution. Heating was again in air at 288°. It is seen that copper was the most powerful oxidation catalyst. The effect was not general as far as adhesives were concerned; apparently the epoxy resin was the substance susceptible to oxidation. Heating in air had only a moderate effect on adhints made with a nylon or with butadiene-acrylonitrile copolymers, whatever the metal.

Observations analogous to those summarized in Table VIII, 2nd column, have been made earlier but remained unexplained.[52] Phenol-formaldehyde adhesives were used to glue two pieces of metal together (as butt joints). The breaking stresses for aluminum adhints and cast iron adhints were similar (e.g., 189 and 179 bars, respectively) but brass gave distinctly lower values (e.g., 39 bars).

In the above examples, adherends caused accelerated decomposition of the adhesive. The inverse effect, namely weakening of the adherends by the adhesive, also is known. It has been repeatedly noticed that wood glued with strongly alkaline adhesives broke near the interface at a stress lower than the breaking stress of the wood before glueing; and this effect was traced to hydrolysis of wood by the adhesive.

Flaws in the Bulk of the Adhesive

§52.   5. THEY ALWAYS APPEAR during setting but usually are particularly conspicuous when (1) impurities are pushed toward the center of the adhesive layer in the course of solidification, see §42, or (2) the number of crystallization nuclei is relatively small and the rate of crystal growth is great, see §40.

There are two main devices for retarding crystal growth: one consists in adding impurities which concentrate at the crystal-liquid boundary, and the other depends on an increase in the viscosity of the liquid. In some instances, the two procedures are entirely different, but in other cases one addition combines both mechanisms.

When a dye is added to a supersaturated solution of a salt, such as NaCl, the resulting salt crystals often are more numerous and less bulky than when the dye was absent; and they are dyed. The amounts of dye introduced usually are so small that they do not markedly affect the viscosity of the solution; thus in these systems the impurity retards crystal growth because the large ion of the dye tries to substitute for the small ion (of the same sign) in the inorganic salt and in this manner disrupts the crystal lattice so badly that this ceases to grow.

The two effects are combined in the retardation of crystal growth by substances of the gelatin type. Also gelatin is an electrolyte, and the gelatin ion (positive or negative, depending on the acidity of the solution) may tend to substitute for the equally charged ion of the salt. But the viscosity effect also will be felt. When a crystal grows, it pushes the liquid with whatever is in it away from the crystal nucleus. Those molecules whose rate of diffusion is great compared with the rate of crystal growth will have time to spread over the bulk of the solution. On the other hand, gelatin molecules, whose diffusion coefficient is extremely small, will not move far. Hence, if the weight-to-volume concentration of gelatin in the solution is x g./cm.^{3} and the volume of the crystal at any stage of its growth is v cm.^{3}, than an amount xv g. of gelatin will be found around the crystal. The viscosity of this layer may be so high that convection currents are suppressed and supply of supersaturated solution to the growing crystal retarded.

When there is no adsorption of the impurity, the effect of the latter is all due to viscosity changes.

The above reasoning explains the fact that the vast majority of adhesives are mixtures. When the least soluble ingredient starts crystallizing on evaporation of the solvent, the other components act as the dye or gelatin in the above examples. An analogous effect takes place when an ingredient starts crystallization during the cooling of a melt. High viscosity or consistency of commercial adhesives, in addition to rendering them tacky, hinders crystallization in them. Many solders are neither polycomponent mixtures nor very viscous in the molten state; they are (after setting) microcrystalline because they are cooled so rapidly that a very large number of nuclei grows at one; thus there are many crystals and, consequently, the average crystal must be small.

Time of Set

§53.   IN SOME INDUSTRIAL APPLICATIONS the achievement of a suitable *rate* of setting is more difficult than that of a satisfactory final strength. Thus, see §38, in automatic glueing of cartons, the adhesive is applied to one flap or both flaps, the flaps are pressed together and are kept under pressure for, say, 5 seconds. Then the carton is pushed away on the conveyer belt.

The setting must progress so far in these 5 seconds that bent flaps do not open up as soon as pressure is removed. The tendency of the flaps to unbend can be depressed by moistening the folds with water but this device apparently is not used in industry; when a higher speed of glueing is required, an adhesive which sets more rapidly is selected.

In other applications the rate of setting should not be too rapid. Time of set should be long enough to enable the operator to place all members of the adhint in the correct position. Application of wall paper is a familiar example of this requirement.

From the point of view of the time of set, the classification of adhesives would be almost identical with that given in §40. Adhesives which solidify on cooling usually have the greatest rate of setting; those solidifying because of a chemical reaction generally need more time, and solvent cements often have the longest time of set.

It does not seem advisable to discuss the rate of setting in detail because it so greatly depends on the composition of the adhesive and on external circumstances.

The rate of cooling is determined above all by the heat conductivities of the materials of the adhint and by the geometry of the system. In theory, the final strength of a bond should depend on the rate of solidification because the tensile (or shear) strength of a solid usually is a function of this rate. Experimentally, this effect seems to be insignificant in the usual adhints.

The rate of chemical reactions which lead to solidification of an adhesive has been measured many times and for many systems. Considerable literature exists on the time of setting of plaster of Paris and of portland cement, and it is known by what additions this time can be extended or shortened. Time needed for optimum curing of innumerable rubber mixes, at many different temperatures, also has been ascertained. Many data are available also on the rate of condensation of phenol-formaldehyde and other polymeric adhesives.

The rapidity of evaporation of solvent from a solvent cement depends on the vapor pressure of the solvent, the ease of convection, the rate of diffusion of solvent molecules through the surface layer of the drying adhesive, and many other variables. If solvent can be lost by imbibition also, the pore number, the pore diameter, the wettability, and other properties of the adherend also will affect the rate of setting.

References

1. McBain, J. W., and Lee, W. B., *J. Phys. Chem.* **31**, 1674 (1927).
2. Konstantinova, W. P., *Acta Physicochim. U.R.S.S.* **1**, 286 (1934).
3. Lasoski, S. W., and Kraus, G., *J. Polymer Sci.* **18**, 359 (1955).
4. Bikerman, J. J., *Adhesive Age* **2**, No. 2, 23 (1959).
5. Bikerman, J. J., and Huang, C.-R., *Trans. Soc. Rheology* **3**, 5(1959/60).
6. Nightingale, S. J., "Tin Solders." Brit. Non-Ferrous Metals Res. Assoc., London, 1932.
7. Bikerman, J. J., "Surface Chemistry," 2nd ed., p. 31. Academic Press, New York, 1958.
8. Delmonte, J., "The Technology of Adhesives." Reinhold, New York, 1947; Epstein, G., "Adhesive Bonding of Metals." Reinhold, New York, 1954.
9. Clash, R. F., and Rynkiewicz, L. M., *Ind. Eng. Chem.* **36**, 279 (1944).
10. Hunter, E., and Oakes, W. G., *Trans. Faraday Soc.* **41**, 49 (1945).
11. Alfrey, T., Goldfinger, G., and Mark, H., *J. Appl. Phys.* **14**, 700 (1943).
12. Sorg, E. H., and Breslau, A. J., *SPE Journal* **13**, No. 6, 115 (1957).
13. Loughborough, D. L., and Haas, E. G., *J. Aeronaut. Sci.* **13**, No. 3, 126 (1946).
14. Tin Research Institute, "Fusible Alloys Containing Tin." Greenford, 1949.
15. Hinken, E., and Marra, A. A., *Forest Prods. J.* **7**, 286 (1957).
16. Truax, T. R., *U. S. Dept. Agr. Bull.* **1500** (1929).
17. Belykh, I. N., *Stroitel. Prom.* **32**, No. 11, 38 (1954); *Chem. Abstr.* **49**, 4255 (1955).
18. Partridge, J. H., "Glass-to-Metal Seals." Soc. Glass Tech., Sheffield, 1949.
19. Rawson, H., *Brit. J. Appl. Phys.* **2**, 151 (1951).
20. Svenson, N. L., *Brit. J. Appl. Phys.* **3**, 30 (1952).
21. Zaid, M., *Brit. J. Appl. Phys.* **3**, 31 (1952).
22. Timoshenko, S., "Strength of Materials," 3rd ed., Part II. Van Nostrand, Princeton, New Jersey, 1956.
23. Hetényi, M., "Beams on Elastic Foundation." Univ. of Mich. Press, Ann Arbor, Michigan, 1946.
24. Dietz, A. G. H., Grinsfelder, H.. and Reissner, E., *Trans. Am. Soc. Mech. Engrs.* **68**, 329 (1946).

25. Kobatake, Y., and Inoue, Y., *Appl. Sci. Research* **A7**, 53 (1957).

26. Inoue, Y., and Kobatake, Y., *Appl. Sci. Research* **A7**, 314 (1958).

27. Shreiner, S. A., and Zubov, P. I., *Doklady Akad. Nauk S.S.S.R.* **124**, 1102 (1959).

28. Kushner, J. B., *Proc. Am. Electroplaters' Soc.* **41**, 188 (1954); *Metal Finishing* **56**, No. 4, 46 (1958).

29. Brenner, A., and Senderoff, S., *Proc. Am. Electroplaters' Soc.* **35**, 53 (1948).

30. Poritsky, H., *Physics* **5**, 406 (1934).

31. Redston, G. D., and Stanworth, J. E., *J. Soc. Glass Technol.* **29**, 48 (1945).

32. Turnbull, J. C., *J. Am. Ceram. Soc.* **41**, 372 (1958).

33. Weatherwax, R. C., Coleman, B., and Tarkow, H., *J. Polymer Sci.* **27**, 59 (1958).

34. Moser, F., *in* "Adhesion and Adhesives," p. 84. Wiley, New York, 1954.

35. Bredzs, N., and Schwartzbart, H., *Welding J.* **37**, 493-s (1958).

36. Bueckle, H., and Blin, J., *J. Inst. Metals* **80**, 385 (1952).

37. Arkharov, V. I., and Mardeshev, S., *Doklady Akad. Nauk S.S.S.R.* **103**, 273 (1955).

38. Josefowitz, D., and Mark, H., *Ind. Rubber World* **106**, 33 (1942).

39. Voyutskii, S. S., Shapovalova, A. I., and Pisarenko, A. P., *Doklady Akad. Nauk S.S.S.R.* **105**, 1000 (1955).

40. Deryagin, B. V., Zherebkov, S. K., and Medvedeva, A. M., *Kolloid Zhur.* **18**, 404 (1956).

41. Bikerman, J. J., *J. Appl. Polymer Sci.* **2**, 216 (1959).

42. Schrader, W. H., and Bodner, M. J., *Plastics Technol.* **3**, 988 (1957).

43. Kreidl, W. H., *Kunststoffe* **49**, 71 (1959).

44. Peukert, H., *Kunststoffe* **48**, 3 (1958).

45. Kobeko, P. P., and Marei, F. I., *Zhur. Tekh. Fiz.* **16**, 277 (1946).

46. Buchan, S., "Rubber to Metal Bonding." Crosby Lockwood, London, 1948.

47. Chadwick, R., *J. Inst. Metals* **62**, 277 (1938).

48. Tylecote, R. F., *J. Inst. Metals* **78**, 301 (1950).

49. Moore, D. G., Mason, M. A., and Harrison, W. N., *J. Am. Ceram. Soc.* **35**, 53 (1952).

50. Moore, D. G., Pitts, J. W., Richmond, J. C., and Harrison, W. N., *J. Am. Ceram. Soc.* **37**, 1 (1954).

51. Black, J. M., and Blomquist, R. F., *Ind. Eng. Chem.* **50**, 918 (1958).

52. Ehlers, J. F., *Kunststoffe* **40**, 151 (1950).

CHAPTER 6

Final Strength of Adhints

§54. Physical and chemical processes in an adhint, which generally are rapid immediately after the application of the adhesive, sometimes continue as long as the assembly exists. However, the rate of this aging as a rule decreases in time so that, see §15, it is possible mentally to separate the state of setting (during which the above processes are quick) from the final state when the properties of the adhint may, at a sufficient approximation, be treated as independent of the age of the system.

The final strength of an adhint is its strength in the final state. The most general statement which can be made concerning ruptures in the final state is that failure occurs where and when the *local stress* exceeds the *local strength*. This can happen in an adherend, a boundary layer, or in the adhesive.

Improbability of True Adhesional Failures

§55. Failures exactly along the adherend–adhesive interface were often postulated in the past. As far as we know now, they occur, if at all, so rarely as to be of no practical importance for the mechanical behavior of adhints. Separation following the interface might perhaps be achieved by special devices, and §57 suggests some experiments for detecting it.

It is clear that a true "failure in adhesion," that is clean parting of unchanged adherend and unchanged adhesive, is impossible whenever a boundary layer exists. In these systems no definite interface is present and, consequently, no interfacial break can be imagined. This statement is still correct if every definite phase in an adhint is considered to belong to adherend or to adhesive. Take, for example, a system of metal–metal oxide–organic polymer. The oxide is a boundary layer but may also be treated as a primer, and break between metal and oxide or between oxide and polymer still might be an instance of an adhesion failure. In reality, however, a sharp frontier between metal and its oxide usually does not exist; first because oxide films on metals are likely to be nonstoichiometric (thus, in aluminum oxide on aluminum, ratio of Al to O gradually decreases from metal to air) and, secondly, because the two lattices (of metal and oxide, respectively) are likely to be distorted for the depth of several atoms on both sides of the imaginary frontier. Thus, instead of a plane interface between a perfect metal lattice and a perfect oxide lattice, as postulated in the "molecular" theories of adhesion, a layer of distorted structure exists, and crack starts where this distortion is particularly severe.

In some instances, see §§28 and 49, the weakest spot of the boundary layer is present not in the defective zone between two phases but is situated definitely in the bulk of the crystals between the metal and the adhesive. That this is "failure in cohesion" cannot be doubted.

§56.   It remains only to discuss why rupture between oxide and polymer is a rare phenomenon. This discussion applies, of course, also to other interfaces; the essential difference between this boundary and the metal-oxide boundary described above is that there is practically no intermixing between oxide (or glass and many other materials) and the polymer and, as far as known, no significant distortion of the lattice of the adherend; the polymers usually are amorphous, that is do not have a definite structure which might be upset by contact with a crystal of another composition. Thus in the instance of metal oxide (or glass, etc.) in contact with a chemically inactive polymer (such as polyethylene) a true interface presumably exists. However, mechanical separation does not progress along this boundary.

In Fig. 52 white circles represent atoms of the adherend and black circles, those of the adhesive. If stress is applied normally to the main plane of phase boundary, §2, a crack will start at a

ADHEREND

CRACK→

CRACK

ADHESIVE

FIG. 52. A proof of the improbability of true failures in adhesion.

point where local stress exceeds local strength. Let us assume
that this point is situated between the adherend and the adhesive, as shown at the left end of the sketch. The crack propa-
gates toward the right, and it can continue either between two
atoms of the adherend, or between an atom of the adherend and
an atom of the adhesive, or between two atoms of the latter.
If these three paths are equally probable, the probability of a
crack (which started between two materials) to continue in the
phase boundary for two atoms is 1/3rd. The probability of an
interfacial crack three atoms long is $(1/3)^2$, and that of an interfacial crack extending over $n + 1$ atoms is $(1/3)^n$. If n is, for
instance, 10, this probability is about 1/59,000; in other words,
only in one adhint for 59,000 will a phase separation 11 atoms
long be found. Thus, no rupture on microscopic or macroscopic
scale can ever occur between two phases.

The above calculation can be refined in three respects, and
each refinement lowers the probability of interfacial detachment.
Factor 1/3 above was arrived at because only three alternative
paths were considered. However, more than one path between
adherend and adherend or between adhesive and adhesive corresponds to each path between adherend and adhesive; this is
better seen on three-dimensional models. Thus, still confining
ourselves to geometry, we may say that a factor of 1/7 would be
more realistic than that of 1/3; for each way between two different atoms we consider 3 ways between identical atoms (along
3 faces of a cube) in each of the two phases.

The second refinement concerns the molecular structure of adhesives. Usually, they are polymers and their representation as an agglomeration of independent atoms is misleading. The right-hand half of Fig. 52 takes the long-chain nature of the adhesives into account. As a rule, it is easier to separate two molecules of a polymer than to break one of the chains. Thus, as soon as the crack reaches the space between two polymer molecules, it will advance in this space until the space between two other polymer chains is reached, and so on; it is clear that in its progress from one intermolecular clearance to another the crack will practically never return to the two-phase boundary.

The third refinement refers to the relative intensity of intermolecular forces between equal and unequal substances. In the van der Waals equation for one mole of gas

$$\left(p + \frac{a}{v^2}\right)(v - b) = RT \tag{65}$$

p is gas pressure, v its volume, T absolute temperature, R gas constant, and a and b are constants characteristic for each gas. In particular, a is a measure of intermolecular attraction. It is known for many years (see, e.g., Beattie[1]) that equation (65) is applicable to gas mixtures also and that a simple (approximate) relation exists between the a values for the mixture and for its components. Let a_1 be the attraction constant for gas No. 1 and a_2 that for gas No. 2. Then the attraction (a_{12}) between molecules of gas No. 1 and those of gas No. 2 is given by the equation

$$\frac{a_1}{a_{12}} = \frac{a_{12}}{a_2}. \tag{66}$$

This relation is not exact but, at any rate, it shows that attraction between two dissimilar molecules is smaller than between two identical "stronger" molecules but greater than between two "weak" molecules. In the instance of a metal–polymer adhint we may conclude that attraction between metal and polymer is greater than between polymer and polymer; hence the bond between two polymer molecules is more likely to be severed than any other bond; thus molecular forces favor rupture in cohesion in the adhesive layer.

It may be mentioned in passing that attraction represented by sign a_{12} is responsible for the coherence of the adhint as long as external forces are too small to start rupture.

A somewhat different proof of the improbability of failure in adhesion can be formulated as follows.

In §61 the probability theory of the tensile strength of brittle solids is outlined. A consequence, supported by the experiment, of this theory is that larger samples are weaker than smaller specimens. Thus, the breaking stress of a short wire or filament is greater than that of a longer piece of an identical material. The numerical value of this difference cannot be stated in precise terms because every sample has its own distribution of flaws. However in many instances the breaking stress decreases to one-half when the filament length increases ten to hundredfold.

As the "thickness of the interface" is very much smaller than the thickness of an adhesive film, breaking stress of the interface must be greater than that of the adhesive. It is, of course, difficult to assess the thickness of the interface, i.e., the thickness of the space between the adjacent rows of adherend and adhesive atoms, but a value near 10^{-9} cm. seems reasonable. The minimum thickness of industrial or household adhesive films may be put equal to 10^{-3} cm. Thus it is 10^6 times as great as the thickness of the interface. With the above-mentioned dependence of breaking stress on thickness, the interface would be between 2^6 and 2^3 times as strong as the bulk. Even if the lowest estimate is accepted, it is clear that in a sandwich of material A and material B, the strength of A being 8 times that of B, material B rather than A regularly will be broken.

If the "three-dimensional interface" and the adhesive film are perfectly plastic rather than brittle bodies, their yield stress at a first approximation would be inversely proportional to their thicknesses, see §67.3; thus adhesive film will yield at a stress one-millionth the yield stress of the "interface."

The third refinement mentioned above in this section would apply to the present reasoning also and would further decrease the probability of rupture between adherend and adhesive.

A cruder method of accounting for the absence of true interfacial ruptures is based on surface roughness, §3. Because of roughness a butt joint, §67, in the immediate vicinity of the interface is a multitude of scarf joints, §74. As scarf joints are relatively strong, adhesive breaks in a space in which a butt joint still may be considered as such, i.e., where rupture still may progress approximately normally to the external force.

§57.   THE REASONING of the preceding section shows that smooth parting of adherend and adhesive is very difficult. A few experiments have been suggested to realize this parting; unfortunately so far they remained suggestions only.

One suggestion[2] refers to epitaxy. Epitaxy, or epitaxis, or oriented overgrowth[3] is orientation of crystals of substance A when they start and continue to grow on crystal B. For instance, if a drop of sodium chloride solution is permitted to evaporate on a cleavage face of galena (PbS), the sodium chloride cubes have their edges parallel to the cube edges of the galena. This alignment takes place because the lattice spacing of NaCl is almost equal to that of PbS and sodium chloride can almost continue the lattice of the "host" substance. When the lattice spacings are very different or complications occur, the new crystals have random orientation on the "host" surface. As in the instance of epitaxis lattice distortion is almost absent, see §55, adhesion of NaCl to PbS may be expected to be strong. Adherence of a crystal showing no epitaxis would be weak as a distorted layer would be present along the interface. If an instance can be found in which this layer is only two atoms thick (one in the adherend and one in the adhesive) then the breaking stress of the bond might, perhaps, be considered as a measure of true adhesion.

According to the other two suggestions, separation between two phases would occur because the direction of the external force would change by 180° exactly at the interface. Let ρ_1 be the density of the adherends and ρ_2 the density of the adhesive. Let the adhint be immersed in a liquid of density ρ_0 such that $\rho_1 > \rho_0 > \rho_2$. Gravitation would try to push the adherend down and the adhesive up, and the force would reverse its direction at the phase boundary. Centrifugal force may be used instead of gravitation.

Analogously, let μ_1 and μ_2 be the magnetic permeability of adherend and adhesive, respectively. If the adhint is immersed in a liquid of magnetic permeability μ_0 and if $\mu_1 > \mu_0 > \mu_2$, then the adherend will tend to move toward a more intensive, and the adhesive toward the less intensive magnetic field. Evidently, dielectric constant and an inhomogeneous electrostatic field can be substituted for magnetic permeability and magnetic field.

§58.   JOINTS failing in adhesion have often been mentioned in the literature. As §56 demonstrates, these statements cannot be correct. Failure occurred either in a weak boundary layer or in the adhesive near the interface. In both instances some foreign matter must have remained on both adherends. Unfortunately the adherends, as a rule, were subjected to a cursory visual inspection only, and adhesion failure was believed to happen if no adhesive was visible on one of the solids. An examination of this kind is inadequate. It is very easy to miss a coating as thick as 20 microns if it is transparent. "Moisture-proof" cellophane is coated on both sides with films about 2 microns thick but it looks exactly as regular cellophane.

There are several methods known for detecting small amounts of foreign matter on a solid. In some instances, contact angle of water (or another liquid) in air is suitable; this is so when the wettabilities of the adhesive or the boundary substance are different from that of the adherend. The coefficient of friction between, say, two metal plates is significantly altered when one of these plates is contaminated with as little as 0.000001 g. of a lubricant per cm.[2]. When the area of the adherend-adhesive boundary is not too small, the amounts of the adhesive remaining on the solid may be sufficient for quantitative or at least qualitative chemical analysis. Electron diffraction is sensitive enough to detect latex imprints on a glass which was touched with an adhesive tape.

An example in which apparently a part of a weak boundary layer was detected on the adherend was recently described.[4]

The clearance between a steel bar and a poly(methyl methacrylate) plug was filled with methyl methacrylate monomer, and the monomer was polymerized *in situ*, e.g., by ultraviolet irradiation. Probably the polymerization was incomplete because, on centrifuging the assembly, rupture took place in the polymer but very near to the interface, and the breaking stress was only about one-sixth the tensile strength of the bulk polymer. After the rupture the steel surface was examined with an ellipsometer, and the conclusion reached that "in no case was the thickness" of foreign matter on the metal "less than the monolayer."

If the adhesive or its weak boundary layer contains radioactive isotopes, the residue clinging to the adherend after the rupture of the joint can be detected and measured with a suitable radiation counter. Experiments of this kind are mentioned in the literature[5] but no complete report seems to be available.

§59. THE EXTREME IMPROBABILITY of a true adhesional failure was first pointed out only a few years ago.[6] Long before this, and repeatedly since, theories of adhesive joints were based on the hypothesis that molecular attraction between adherend and adhesive directly determined the measurable strength of an adhint. It may be worthwhile to scrutinize some of these theories and to indicate some weaknesses specific to each.

1. Let specific free surface energy of an adherend be γ_1 and the corresponding quantity for the solid adhesive be γ_2, and let γ_{12} be the specific free energy of the interface between adherend and adhesive. If the adhint is broken and rupture proceeds exactly along the interface, then the process of rupture results in disappearance of the interface and formation of two solid–air surfaces. For unit area the change in the free surface energy is thus $\Delta\Omega = \gamma_1 + \gamma_2 - \gamma_{12}$.

Several scientists identified $\Delta\Omega$ with the work W needed to break an adhint in which the area of the adherend–adhesive interface is equal to unity. Experimentally, W usually is much greater than any probable value of $\Delta\Omega$. The quantity $\Delta\Omega$ can have only more or less probable values because none of the energies γ_1, γ_2, and γ_{12} can be conveniently measured. It is generally believed, however, that 1000 ergs/cm.^{2} is the most likely order of magnitude for these quantities and also for the difference $\gamma_1 + \gamma_2 - \gamma_{12}$. To calculate W we consider a butt joint between two cylinders (basis to basis), each 5 cm. long and made of a material whose modulus of elasticity is 7×10^{11} dynes/cm.^{2} ($\approx 10^7$ psi) as for aluminum. If the breaking stress of the joint is 7×10^8 baryes ($\approx 10^3$ psi), the cylinders are extended by 0.01%, i.e., both cylinders together are in the moment of rupture by 0.001 cm. longer than before the application of the load. Hence, W per unit area is $7 \times 10^8 \times 10^{-3} = 700 \times 10^3$ ergs/cm.^{2} Thus $W = 700 \, \Delta\Omega$.

It is plain that the hypothesis $\Delta\Omega = W$ is wrong not only because there is no separation between two different materials but also because the work of breaking an adhint is spent above all on the deformation of the system before actual rupture takes place. This statement is true also for peeling and other types of rupture.

2. Many investigators believed (and still believe) that a strong attraction between the molecules of the adherend and those of the adhesive is required for a strong bond. A valence bond between an adherend atom and an adhesive atom would be ideal but interaction between dipoles in the two phases also would be admissible.

This hypothesis is easily refuted by the observation that substances (such as polyethylene) which contain no dipoles perfectly adhere to solids (such as glasses, metals, polymers) with which no chemical reaction is possible, see §48. When a chemical reaction undoubtedly occurs, it may result in a weakening of adhints, see §49. When a brittle polar, a brittle nonpolar, and a ductile nonpolar adhesives are compared, the two brittle materials behave similarly, while there is no similarity in the behavior of the two nonpolar substances, see §80.

3. Electrostatic attraction between adherend and adhesive was supposed to be responsible for the major part of the final strength of an adhint. However, in peeling tests, irradiation of the 3-phase line with X-rays or with the rays of radioactive thorium usually increased the work of peeling.[7] As such an irradiation ionizes air around the adhint and thus suppresses the

effects of static electricity, it would reduce the resistance to peeling to almost nothing if this resistance were of electrostatic origin. If the hypothesis were correct, the strength of adhints would have been markedly greater in dry than in humid air; unless the adhesive itself is moisture-sensitive no such effect has been detected yet.

4. Intermixing of adherend and adhesive along their common boundary was believed to be essential. As mentioned in §55, this intermixing certainly takes place in numberless adhints, but it is not necessary because joints between mutually immiscible solids are, if they are proper joints, just as strong as those in which mixing is manifest.

Final Strength of Proper Joints

§60.   IF THE CONCEPT on which this monograph is based is correct, that is if practically every failure of an adhint takes place *in* a material rather than *between* two different materials, then the breaking stress of the adhint must be related to the strength of its weakest phase. This conclusion is confirmed by many observations but, unfortunately, the relation between the strength of a system and that of the weakest material in it is complex and varies from instance to instance.

We base our discussion of this relation on equation

$$\xi = (\alpha f_m + s)\beta \tag{67}$$

although this is rather a mnemonic help than mathematical truth. ξ is molecular cohesion, f_m is breaking stress, s is "frozen stress," and α and β are stress concentration factors defined in the following.

Molecular cohesion ξ is force (per unit area) needed to move apart two halves of a body supposed to have no blemishes of any kind; it is a property of the molecular (or atomic) structure of the substance and in some instances can be calculated.

The calculation is relatively straightforward for the simple ionic crystals such as those of sodium chloride. If only the electrostatic forces acting between ions at all distances and the repulsive forces significant at distances less than 1 angstrom are considered, cohesion comes out equal to 2.3×10^{10} baryes (330,000 psi) for NaCl; if also dispersion forces are taken into account, the result is 2.6×10^{10} baryes.[8] The usual experimental values are confined between 4×10^7 and 6×10^7 baryes. For polymers, different values are obtained according to whether rupture involves breaking of primary valence bond or can proceed between molecules. In the first alternative, tensile strength would be as high as 4.3×10^{11} baryes (6,000,000 psi) for a phenolformaldehyde resin[8] and 1.5×10^{11} baryes for a cellulose fiber.[9] If no degradation of molecular chains takes place, the theoretical cohesion may be about 4×10^9 baryes for phenolformaldehyde condensation products and near 3×10^9 for cellulose, that is of the experimental order of magnitude. However, the idealized structure postulated for the calculation of strength without intramolecular rupture probably never occurs in real polymers. Thus, in general, ξ is much greater than the experimental breaking stress averaged over the affected area; see also §82.

Letter f_m in equation (67) denotes this stress. In the instance of butt joints $f_m = F_m/A_1$, F_m being the external force and A_1 the cross section of the adhint in a plane perpendicular to F_m. For lap joints stressed in tension, $f_m = F_m/A_2$, F_m having the previous meaning and A_2 being the area of the overlap. The values of f_m for some other types of adhint are given in Chapter VII.

Factor α is different from unity because the stress at the "crucial" point, that is at the point of incipient fracture, is not the average stress and deviates from it more the greater the difference in the mechanical properties of adherend and adhesive. If adhesive and adherend were identical, α would have been equal to unity. The magnitude of α in various adhints is discussed in Chapter VII.

The "frozen stress" s has been referred to in §43 (as shrinkage and swelling stresses). It has to be vectorially added to, or vectorially subtracted from, stress αf_m caused by external force F_m.

The sum $\alpha f_m + s$ would be equal to molecular cohesion if the adhesive were uniform down to molecular dimensions. It has to be multiplied by factor β because no solid is truly uniform. The discrepancy between the theoretical values of cohesion, as stated above in this section, and the experimental breaking stresses of solids has been accounted for by flaws in real solids. It is believed that every rupture originates at a bad flaw or a particularly weak spot, and that weak spots are distributed in the solid more or less at random.

Thus the theory has two aspects. First, we must render the existence of flaws probable and gain a knowledge of their distribution. Secondly, we must consider the possible nature of these flaws and prove that flaws which are likely to be present can be the cause of the striking difference between theoretical and experimental strength.

§61.   THE PROBABILITY THEORY of strength is at least as old as Plateau's work. (Leonardo da Vinci is said to have forecast it but no clear indication of the theory could be found by the present author in Leonardo's available notes.) Plateau[10] noticed that big foam films lasted for a shorter time than small films from an identical solution and concluded that this size effect presumably was due simply to the greater probability of a weak spot (caused by an external agent) in a larger specimen.

An early mathematical treatment of the theory was published by Peirce.[11] Suppose that N_0 samples were tested and N of these broke at stresses between f and $f + df$. (The subscript m used in §60 to remind the reader that we were dealing with the maximum possible stresses is omitted here.) Evidently, $(N/N_0) = \varphi(f)$ is a function of f. The probability that the strength of one of these samples is equal to, or greater than, f is $\int_f^\infty \varphi(f)\, df$.

Let the length of each sample be l cm. If we now consider a sample nl cm. long, we can apply this reasoning to each part, l cm. long, of the large specimen. The probability Π that none of the n regions of this specimen will break at a stress below f is equal to the product of the probabilities for each region. Thus

$$\Pi = \left[\int_f^\infty \varphi(f)\, df \right]^n$$

or, if N_0 specimens of length nl are tested, the number breaking at a stress between f and $f + df$ is given by

$$N = \varphi(f) \left[\int_f^\infty \varphi(f)\, df \right]^n \cdot df.$$

Function $\varphi(f)$ can either be postulated or can be derived from experiments; for instance, for cotton fibers, it was found that

$$f_{nf} - f_l = -4.2(1 - n^{-0.2})\sigma_l$$

σ_l being the standard deviation of the breaking stresses found for length l; f_{nl} is the mean breaking stress of specimens nl cm. long and f_l that for l cm. long specimens.

A particularly simple test of the probability theory of fracture is conducted as follows.[12, 13] Determine the *average* breaking stress of samples nl cm. long (or adhints nh cm. thick). Determine the *minimum* breaking stress in a group of n samples, each l cm. long, or h cm. thick. These two stresses should be equal because in each set of experiments the strength of the weakest spot along nl (or nh) cm. is measured. Experimental results confirmed the expectation for glass fibers and also for many other substances (see, e.g., reference 14) so that the theory may be considered a reliable guide.

§62. THE DEGREE OF WEAKENING caused by flaws requires a somewhat more extended treatment. This treatment leads to quantitative results if the adhesive is a Hookean solid or, see §65, behaves as a Hookean solid after the deformation caused by an external force. Also, the member containing flaws must be two-dimensional only, as the mathematics becomes prohibitively difficult as soon as the third dimension is involved.

Imagine, therefore, a thin foil (of width w) in which a circle of radius r_0 has been cut out, see Fig. 53; w is supposed to be greater than about $5r_0$. If the foil is stretched by force $F = fw\delta$, δ being the thickness of the foil ($w \gg \delta$), then[15] stress σ_ρ normal to the circumference is given by

$$\sigma_\rho = 0.5f[(1 - \rho^2) + (1 - 4\rho^2 + 3\rho^4) \cos 2\psi]; \qquad (68)$$

ρ is r_0/r, if r is the distance of a point in the foil from the center of the circle and ψ is angle between the direction of the external force and the radius connecting the center of the circle with the point for which equation (68) is valid. When $r = r_0$ and $\rho = 1$, that is at the phase boundary, $\sigma_\rho = 0$ as we assume that the inside of the hole cannot support any stress; if the hole is filled with a material weaker than the foil but still able to transmit stresses the equation must be modified. At $r \gg r_0$ the value of ρ is negligibly small and stress $\sigma_\rho = (f/2)(1 + \cos 2\psi)$; thus stress in the direction of the external force (i.e., at $\psi = 0$) is equal to f as it should be. At $\psi = 0$, stress σ_ρ rapidly decreases from f to zero on nearing the hole; at $\rho = 0.5$, σ_ρ is still $0.47 f$, at $\rho = 0.8$ it is $0.34 f$, and so on.

Stress σ_ψ along the circumference of the hole and along circles concentric with it is given by equation

$$\sigma_\psi = 0.5f[(1 + \rho^2) - (1 + 3\rho^4) \cos 2\psi]. \tag{68a}$$

It is, when $\psi = 0$, zero at $\rho = 0$, i.e., far from the hole. At the phase boundary (that is at $\rho = 1$) $\sigma_\psi = f(1 - 2 \cos 2\psi)$ and at the right-hand and the left-hand ends of the circle, see Fig. 53,

$$\sigma_\psi = 3f. \tag{69}$$

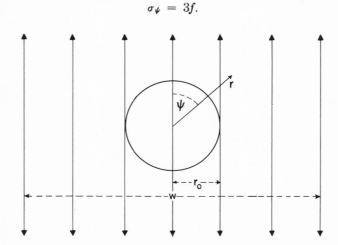

Fig. 53. Stress concentration at a circular hole.

Thus the pull in the direction of the external force at the points where the tangents to the circle are parallel to this force is 3 times as great as the average pull. In this instance, β of §60 is equal to 3.

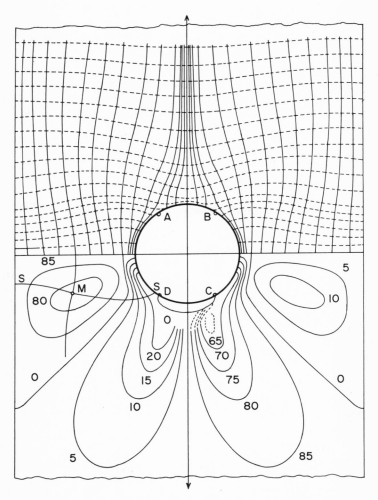

Fɪɢ. 54. Experimental stress concentration at a circular hole. From reference 15.

Figure 54 demonstrates an experimental confirmation of equation (68a). It was prepared on the basis of an optical examination of a polymer plate, 2.64 cm. wide, having a round hole of 0.8 cm. diameter and stressed in the direction of the arrows. The upper half of the figure shows the direction of the principal stresses, and in the lower half the isoclines are drawn; the direction of the principal stress is constant along each isocline. The numbers at the isoclines mean the deviation of this direction (in degrees of an angle) from the direction of the external force. Thus the (solid) lines of the principal stress in the right-hand upper quarter of the figure are inclined from SW to NE near the equatorial line, and from SE to NW near the top; somewhere in between they are directed from N to S, and line marked 0 in the bottom half is the locus of these points.

Shear stress τ is

$$\tau = 0.5f(1 + 2\rho^2 - 3\rho^4) \sin 2\psi. \tag{70}$$

It is zero along the circumference of the hole because of its symmetry. It is greatest at $\sin 2\psi = 1$, i.e., at $\psi = 45°$ and at $\rho = (1/3)^{0.5}$.

§63.   THE GREATEST STRESS concentration factor at a circular flaw is equal to 3. Much greater factors are possible when the hole is elliptical. In Fig. 55 the principal stress lines in the vicinity of such a hole are illustrated. If a is the half-axis of the ellipse perpendicular to the external force and b the half-axis parallel to the latter, then stress σ_ψ at the right-hand and the left-hand extremes of the ellipse is

$$\sigma_\psi = f\left(1 + \frac{2a}{b}\right) \tag{71}$$

As a may be much greater than b (as in a crack), the stress concentration factor

$$\beta = 1 + \frac{2a}{b} \tag{72}$$

may be a large number. If, for instance, $a = 100b$, then $\beta = 201$, that is the maximum stress acting in the adhesive is 201 times the average stress.

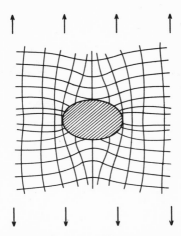

FIG. 55. Stress concentration at an elliptical hole. From reference 15.

If the ellipse is extended in the direction of the external force, rather than normal to it as in Fig. 55, then a is smaller than b and the stress concentration is less significant. If $a \ll b$, the value of β is practically equal to unity. Thus a crack along the line of pull has no harmful effect.

§64.   IF THE HOLE is a square, the highest β is observed at the corners. The actual values of β depend on the sharpness of these corners (which cannot be infinitely sharp because of the molecular structure of matter). Thus, when the radius of curvature at the corners decreases from $0.060l$ to $0.014l$, l being the length of a side of the square, β near the corners increases from 3.9 to 6.2.

If the hole is a rectangle, the greatest β depends on the ratio of its length to its width and also on the angle ψ between the longer side of the rectangle and the direction of force. If, for instance, this angle increases from 30° to 60°, the maximum β (for the above ratio equal to 5) increases from 7 to 12.

If there are two circular holes in the plate, their effect depends on their mutual distance $2\lambda r_o$, see Fig. 56, and on the direction of the external force. When the force acts parallel to $0y$, two holes weaken the plate more than one hole does but the

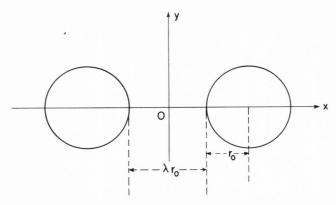

FIG. 56. Stresses in a plate perforated with two circular holes.

difference is small if λ is greater than 1.5; at $\lambda = 1.5$ the greatest β is 3.26 but at $\lambda = 2.0$ it is 3.02, that is practically equal to that at $\lambda = \infty$. When the force acts along $0x$, two holes are less dangerous than one because they are like an ellipse elongated parallel to the pull direction, §63. Thus, the maximum value of β is 2.57 for $\lambda = 1$.

§65. THE CONCLUSIONS reported in §§62 to 64 are derived from equilibrium equations. In other words, it is assumed that no movement occurs and that the shape of the holes is that *after*, not before the application of the external force.

It would be advantageous to be able to predict the difference between the two shapes but the present theories apparently cannot give final answers to this problem. It is clear, however, that both elastic and plastic changes tend to reduce the value of β. If, for instance, the hole was a circle before the application of stress, either elastic or plastic deformation will alter it to an ellipse elongated in the pull direction, that is will render a smaller than b, see §63, and thus lower the value of β under its initial magnitude of 3.0. If the total elongation is large, say over 100%, every circular or quadratic hole will be extended into an ellipse-like hole directed along the lines of force, so that flaws present in the adhesive before the tension was applied will be made innocuous. If, on the other hand, the total relative elongation is small, say less than 3%, the deformation occurring before the rupture will not be able markedly to influence the shape of the weak spots, and stress concentrations will be approximately as great as calculated in §§62 to 64.

REFERENCES

1. Beattie, J. A., *Chem. Revs.* **44**, 141 (1949).
2. Bikerman, J. J., *in* "Adhesion," p. 27. Soc. Chem. Ind., London, 1952.
3. See, e.g., Bikerman, J. J., "Surface Chemistry," 2nd ed., p. 274. Academic Press, New York, 1958.
4. Patrick, R. L., Doede, C. M., and Vaughan, W. A., *J. Phys. Chem.* **61**, 1036 (1957).
5. Bright, W. M., *in* "Adhesion and Adhesives. Fundamentals and Practice," p. 33. Wiley, New York, 1954.
6. Bikerman, J. J., *J. Colloid Sci.* **2**, 163 (1947).
7. Deryagin, B. V., and Krotova, N. A., "Adgeziya," p. 73. Acad. Sci. U.S.S.R., Moscow, 1949.
8. de Boer, J. H., *Trans. Faraday Soc.* **32**, 10 (1938).
9. Mark, H., *in* "Cellulose and Cellulose Derivatives" (E. Ott, ed.), p. 1000. Interscience, New York, 1943.
10. Plateau, J., *Mém. acad. roy. sci. Belg.* **37** 9th ser., 7 (1869).
11. Peirce, F. T., *Textile Inst. J.* **17**, T 355 (1926).
12. Bikerman, J. J., *J. Soc. Chem. Ind. (London)* **60**, 23 (1941).
13. Bikerman, J. J., and Passmore, G. H., *Glass Ind.* **29**, 144 (1948).
14. Greene, C. H., *J. Am. Ceram. Soc.* **39**, 66 (1956).
15. Savin, G. N., "Kontsentratsiya napryazhenii okolo otverstii," p. 97. GITTL., Moscow-Leningrad, 1951. (Also a German edition is available: "Spannungserhöhung am Rande von Löchern.")

CHAPTER 7

Stresses in Adhints

§66. STRESS CONCENTRATION at flaws as discussed in §§62 to 65 exists in every solid and thus is not characteristic for adhesive joints as such. In this chapter stress concentrations near the adherend–adhesive boundary are considered. The corresponding stress concentration factors are denoted by letter α in §60; as mentioned there, α generally would be unity if the adherend and adhesive had identical mechanical properties.

Unfortunately, calculation of α has not yet been carried out in a fully satisfactory manner for any type of adhint or any type of fracture. Thus the following review is a crude approximation only. It is believed, however, that even a crude approximation might be helpful in understanding the behavior of real adhints.

The subject can be systematized either according to the type of adhint and of the external action, or according to the rheological class of the adhesive (Hookean solids, perfectly plastic solids, and so on). The first-named arrangement has been selected for this book; thus we start with butt joints stressed in tension and complete the list with peeling.

Butt Joints

§67. 1. IF THE ADHINT consists of two cylinders joined basis to basis, external pull applied along the common axis of the two cyinders would cause a "geometrical" concentration of stress.

Let r be the radius of the cylinders and of the adhesive "pancake" before straining, see Fig. 57. Let the thickness of the adhesive film be h before and $h + \Delta h$ after straining, and suppose that the adhint was annealed, keeping the distance $h + \Delta h$ constant, until the stresses induced by the external force relaxed

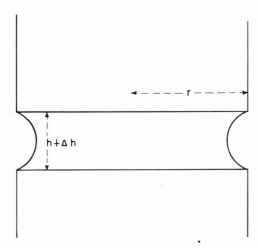

FIG. 57. Geometrical stress concentration in a butt joint.

to become insignificant. If ν is Poisson's ratio for the adhesive and if the cylinders are treated as absolutely rigid, the change Δr in the *average* radius of the adhesive disc is approximately

$$\Delta r = -\nu r \frac{\Delta h}{h}. \tag{73}$$

The actual radial shrinkage of r will, however, depend on the distance of the considered point from the adherend–adhesive interface. At the interface, shrinkage must be zero; and it will have a maximum value in the central horizontal plane of the disc. Thus, the boundary between adhesive and air will be concave toward air, as shown in Fig. 57. The vertical cross section of the concavity may be approximated as a half-ellipse, whose horizontal half-axis will be a little greater than the average Δr of equation (73) (say, equal to $2\Delta r$) and whose vertical half-axis will be $0.5(h + \Delta h)$, i.e., approximately $h/2$. The ratio of the two half-axes will thus amount to about $4\Delta r/h$ or $4\nu r(\Delta h/h^2)$. This ratio corresponds to a/b in equation (72); hence, stress concentration factor

$$\alpha = 1 + 8\nu r \frac{\Delta h}{h^2}. \tag{74}$$

If, for instance, $8\nu = 3$, $\Delta h/h = 0.033$, and $r/h = 100$, then $\alpha = 11$.

2. Usually, however, deformation such as depicted in Fig. 57 will be associated with stresses resisting deformation. Apparently these stresses can be approximately calculated by the methods explained in §43. If the initial external radius of the cylinders and of the disc was r, see Fig. 58, and stress f was ap-

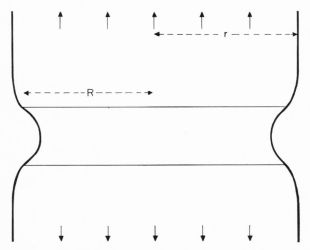

Fig. 58. Stresses caused by Poisson contraction in a butt joint.

plied parallel to their axis, the radius of an unattached cylinder would decrease to $r[1 - (\nu_1 f/E_1)]$, ν_1 and E_1 being the Poisson ratio and the modulus of elasticity of the adherend. Analogously, the radius of the unattached adhesive would be $r[1 - (\nu_2 f/E_2)]$, ν_2 and E_2 standing for Poisson's ratio and Young's modulus of the adhesive material. The actual radius of the circle where the adherend and the adhesive meet is R. Thus, the adherend at the interface is contracted from $r[1 - (\nu_1 f/E_1)]$ to R, while the adhesive is extended from $r[1 - (\nu_2 f/E_2)]$ to R; we assume that ν_2/E_2 is greater than ν_1/E_1. Hence, x_1 of §43 is equal to $r - (r\nu_1 f/E_1) - R$ and $x_2 = R - r + (r\nu_2 f/E_2)$; consequently λ of equation (52) is

$$\lambda = \frac{rf}{R}\left(\frac{\nu_2}{E_2} - \frac{\nu_1}{E_1}\right). \tag{75}$$

If this λ is introduced in equations (53) to (57), the values of tension P and moment M acting along the 3-phase line are obtained.

A numerical example will show the order of magnitude which may be expected for P and the stress caused by this tension. First we approximate (75) as

$$\lambda \approx \frac{f}{2E_2}, \tag{76}$$

i.e., we assume the Young modulus of the adherend to be much greater than that of the adhesive, $r \approx R$ and $\nu_2 \approx 0.5$. With this assumption we may also write

$$P \approx 4\beta^3 D_2 \lambda R \tag{77}$$

instead of (56). Introducing the expressions for β and D_2 from §43 and that for λ from (76), we arrive at the expression

$$P = \frac{\delta^{1.5} f}{2[3(1 - \nu^2)]^{0.25} R^{0.5}} \tag{78}$$

which may be simplified to

$$P \approx \frac{\delta^{1.5} f}{2R^{0.5}}. \tag{79}$$

Let $r(\approx R)$ be equal to 100δ; then $P \approx f\delta/20$. If $\delta = 0.1$ cm., $P \approx 0.005 f$ g./sec^2. This tension must be distributed over an interfacial layer whose thickness will be determined by the roughness of the adherend. Let this thickness be 10^{-4} cm., see §7. In this particular instance, radial stress which causes contraction $r[1 - (\nu_1 f/E_1)] - R$ and expansion $R - r[1 - (\nu_2 f/E_2)]$ in adherend and adhesive, respectively, would be $\sigma_r = 50 f$ g./cm.sec.^{2} Thus, radial stress may considerably exceed the axial stress caused by the external force. In other words, α of equation (67) may reach the value of 50.

It is true that the above calculation is very crude, first of all because the theory of beams on elastic foundation is only a first approximation. Nevertheless the existence of considerable radial stresses along the 3-phase boundary cannot be doubted. These stresses are dangerous not only because of their magnitude but also because of their direction. Suppose that the worst cracks in the adhesive are oriented normally to the adherend-adhesive boundary; in this case their presence would not markedly affect the strength of the adhesive disc, see §63. But these cracks will greatly lower the strength in the radial direction. If factor β of §63 is, say, 1.4 for axial stresses and 11 for radial stresses (i.e., if a/b in equation (72) is 0.2 in the axial and consequently is 5 in the radial direction), radial stress will start fracture even if σ_r is only a fraction (one-seventh) of the axial stress.

A more elaborate calculation[1] (see also reference 2), permits calculation of the stress concentration factor at the center of the adhint, at the middle of the adhesive–air boundary, and at the 3-phase line. Experimental analysis of the stress distribution in butt joints in tension is in, at least qualitative, agreement with the predictions of the theory. Figure 59 shows a typical photoelastic fringe pattern of a stressed butt joint.[3] Two metal plates were glued together with a commercial epoxy adhesive, the width of the plates (from left to right in the figure) being 20 times the thickness of the adhesive film (downward from the top of the figure), and the fringes produced by compressing the sand-

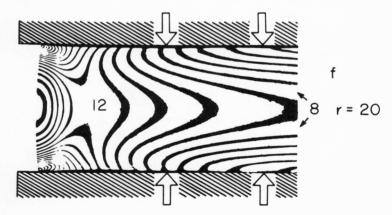

Fig. 59. Photoelastic fringe pattern of a stressed butt joint. From reference 3.

wich, see the arrows, were photographed. The pattern produced by compression ought to be analogous to that produced by tension as long as both compression and tension are small. The left-hand end of the figure represents an edge of the adhesive, while the center of the adhesive film is far to the right of the picture. The stress gradient, i.e., the rate of change of stress with distance, is greater the more crowded the fringes. As number 8 at the right end of the figure indicates, there are only 7 fringes between the center of the film and the part photographed; thus, the stress near the center is almost independent of the distance from the center. However, stress rapidly varies with distance near the middle of the adhesive–air boundary and, particularly, at the 3-phase line. The stress concentration factor at this line is approximately equal to three.

3. The deformations considered in §§67.1 and 2 are purely elastic. The opposite extreme is afforded by rigid-plastic bodies. These fictitious materials show no deformation whatsoever as long as the local shearing stress is below a value which here is denoted by k; and as soon as k is reached, the material starts plastic flow. When there is flow, transformation of mechanical work into heat must occur, that is, viscosity effects should be taken into account. However, in the approximate theory, due chiefly to Prandtl (1923), time effects are disregarded; in other words, only an extremely slow motion is considered. With this restriction also the inertia terms are excluded.

If two flat plates, see Fig. 60, very long in the direction perpendicular to the plane of the page and having width w much greater than the distance h_0 between the plates, are glued together and an average pull f is applied parallel to the y axis, the tensile stress σ_y in the adhesive (parallel to y) may be taken to be independent of y. However, tensile stress σ_x acting parallel to x will depend on both x and y; this stress causes flow of the adhesive toward the plane of $x = 0$ when the plates are pulled apart, analogously to the pressure gradient causing the centripetal flow of a Newtonian liquid in Stefan's experiments, §§25 and 31. In addition, there are shearing stresses. If $abcd$ in Fig. 60 is a rectangle in the xy plane in the adhesive, and if $\overline{ab} = \overline{cd} =$

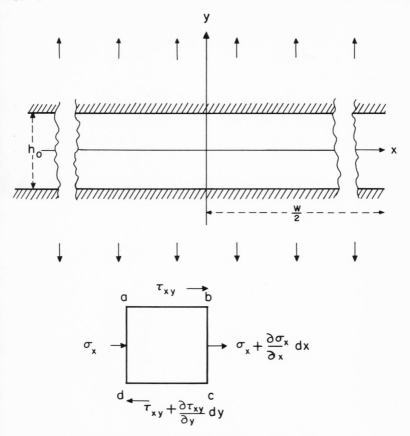

Fig. 60. Stresses in a rigid-plastic adhesive film.

dx and $\overline{ad} = \overline{cb} = dy$, the tension originating from the gradient of σ_x along x and pushing the rectangle to the right is $(\partial\sigma_x/\partial x)$ $dx \cdot dy$. If the shearing stress along ab is τ_{xy} (meaning a stress acting parallel to axis x on a plane whose normal is parallel to axis y) and that along cd is $\tau_{xy} + (\partial\tau_{xy}/\partial y)\cdot dy$, the tension (g./sec.^{2}) originating from these stresses and pushing the rectangle to the left is $(\partial\tau_{xy}/\partial y)\cdot dy\cdot dx$. In equilibrium,

$$\frac{\partial\sigma_x}{\partial x} + \frac{\partial\tau_{xy}}{\partial y} = 0. \tag{80}$$

There is, of course, no such equilibrium when accelerated flow takes place; thus we really determine the force which is just insufficient to cause plastic deformation. Analogously to (80),

$$\frac{\partial \sigma_y}{\partial y} + \frac{\partial \tau_{yx}}{\partial x} = 0$$

or, as $\partial \sigma_y / \partial y = 0$,

$$\frac{\partial \tau_{yx}}{\partial x} = \frac{\partial \tau_{xy}}{\partial x} = 0. \tag{81}$$

The local shearing stress, that first reaches the value k at which motion starts, in general is not parallel to either y or x axis. Its directions are those of *slip lines*. A few slip lines are indicated in Fig. 61; they cross each other at right angles. If a slip

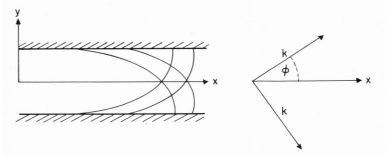

Fig. 61. Slip lines in a rigid-plastic film.

line at a point makes an angle ϕ with the x direction, then the other slip line at the same point makes, with the same direction, an angle $\phi - (\pi/2)$. If stress k acts along one cm. of the first slip line, see Fig. 61, the projection of the tension on the x axis is $k \cdot \cos^2 \phi$ (because the length along the x axis is cos ϕ) and the projection of the corresponding tension acting along the second slip line is $-k \cdot \sin^2 \phi$. Thus, shearing stress τ_{xy} along the x direction is

$$\tau_{xy} = k(\cos^2\phi - \sin^2\phi) = k \cdot \cos 2\phi. \tag{82}$$

It can be shown in an analogous manner that

$$\sigma_x = -p - k \cdot \sin 2\phi \qquad (83)$$

and

$$\sigma_y = -p + k \cdot \sin 2\phi \qquad (84)$$

p being the hydrostatic pressure (acting equally in all directions) caused by external stress f. From (82) to (84) we conclude that

$$\sigma_x = \sigma_y - 2\,k \cdot \sin 2\phi = \sigma_y - 2\,k \left(1 - \frac{\tau_{xy}^2}{k^2}\right)^{0.5} \qquad (85)$$

As neither k nor τ depend on x, see equation (81), equation (80) affords

$$\frac{\partial \sigma_y}{\partial x} + \frac{\partial \tau_{xy}}{\partial y} = 0, \qquad (86)$$

an equation in which σ_y is independent of y and τ_{xy} is independent of x. If τ_{xy} is expressed as $aky + b$, a and b being constants to be determined from the boundary conditions, $\partial \tau_{xy}/\partial y = ak$ and, consequently, $\partial \sigma_y/\partial x = -ak$ and

$$\sigma_y = -akx + kc,$$

kc being the integration constant. As Fig. 61 indicates, slip lines are tangential to the plates; thus at the plates, i.e., at $y = h_0/2$, the angle $\phi = 0$ and $\tau_{xy} = k$, see equation (82). At $y = 0$, $\tau_{xy} = 0$ because of symmetry. Thus, $a = 2/h_0$ and $b = 0$, i.e.,

$$\tau_{xy} = 2ky/h_0 \qquad (87)$$

and

$$\sigma_y = -\frac{2kx}{h_0} + kc. \qquad (88)$$

From the conditions near the adhesive–air boundary it can be shown[4] that constant c is approximately $-\pi/2$. Thus, except near the plane of $x = 0$, x/h_0 is greater than $-c$ whenever $w/2$ is much greater than h_0, i.e., in practically all joints. Thus we may write

$$\sigma_y = -2kx/h_0.$$

The force on a plate l cm. deep (normally to the plane of the drawing) and w cm. wide is

$$- \int_0^w l \frac{2k}{h_0} x \, dx = - \frac{w^2 lk}{h_0}$$

and the average stress is $-wk/h_0$. It is balanced by the external stress f which, consequently, is equal to

$$f = wk/h_0. \tag{89}$$

An analogous calculation for the case of two circular discs of radius a gives

$$f = \frac{2ka}{3h_0}, \tag{90}$$

see, e.g., references 5 and 6

It is instructive to compare equations (89) and (90) with equations (20) and (23). Evidently, there is an analogy between k and η/t, which have identical dimensions (g./cm.sec.²). However, f for Newtonian flow is proportional to $(w/h)^2$ or $(a/h)^2$ while f for plastic flow is proportional to w/h or a/h; here h stands for h_2 in (20) and (23), h_1 in (35), and h_0 in (89) and (90).

In both instances the calculated f would increase without limit as long as a/h increases, i.e., ever thinner adhints are tested. At large a/h values, adherends may break before a plastic adhesive starts flowing. Experiments concerning this conclusion are referred to in §86.

§68.   In the use of adhints their ultimate strength usually is the essential property, and the deformation of the adhesive during straining, at least in the elastic range of stresses, is of importance only insofar as it affects stress distribution in the adhint. It is, however, interesting to know whether the deformation is as it would be expected from the properties of the adhesive in bulk or is specifically altered by the presence of the adherends. Thus, we may ask whether, e.g., the modulus of elasticity and the yield stress of a substance are or are not identical when determined on a bulk specimen or on a specimen in which this substance is present as a thin adhesive film. The main difficulty of this study is due to the thinness of the "glue line," §15. If, for

instance, the cement film in a butt joint cracks when its total
relative elongation is 2%, and the initial thickness of the film is
0.002 cm., the total elongation is 0.00004 cm. and the measuring
instrument should be sensitive to 0.0000004 cm. if we want the
elongation to be measured to 1%.

One way of overcoming this difficulty is to prepare a pile of
adhints, see Fig. 62, and to measure the extension of the whole
pile when tensile forces are applied to it as shown; the adherend
discs are shaded and the adhesive films are white. The extension
of the adherends usually can be determined fairly accurately,
and the extension of the adhesive is the difference between the
total extension of the pile and that of the adherends in it. If the

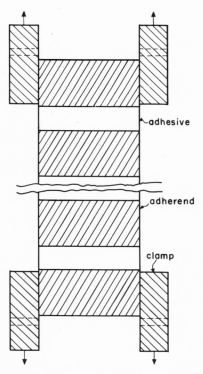

Fig. 62. A pile of adhints for the determination of the stress-strain curves
of the adhesive.

pile contains n adhesive films, the effect looked for is magnified n times.

In another attempt[7] butt joints were used as electrostatic capacitors. At a first approximation, the capacity (C) of a butt joint is inversely proportional to the thickness h of the cement (assumed to be an electrical insulator). Thus, when the adhint is axially strained and the adhesive thickness increases, C decreases. As very sensitive devices for measuring electrostatic capacity exist, this method would be very suitable. Unfortunately, capacity is proportional also to the dielectric constant (ϵ) of the adhesive, and ϵ varies when the adhesive is stretched. Thus, C depends on the ratio ϵ/h rather than on h alone, and the effect of h on ϵ has to be ascertained before changes in h can be computed from the experimental changes in C.

Figure 63 is an example of stress-strain curves obtained by the capacity method. Tensile force in pounds weight (multiply by 4.45×10^5 to obtain it in dynes) is plotted along the ordinate, and the relative elongation of the adhesive is the abscissa.

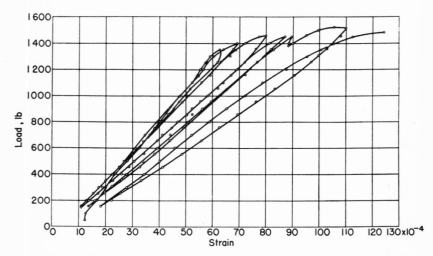

FIG. 63. Stress-strain curves of an adhesive, calculated from electrostatic capacity. Abscissa: relative elongation. Ordinate: tensile force in pounds weight. A methacrylate resin between steel cylinders. From reference 7.

Short steel cylinders (1.27 cm. in diameter) glued with a methacrylate cement made up the adhint; the initial film thickness was approximately 0.004 cm. The load was gradually raised to almost 1200 lb., then lowered to about 100 lb., raised again, and so on. Apparently the methacrylate resin was elastically deformed by loads smaller than 1000 lb. but flowed at higher loads. The apparent modulus of elasticity of a fresh sample at small stresses was about 5×10^{10} g./cm.sec.^{2}

The elastic modulus E and the viscous modulus E_v of the adhesive can be calculated from an experimental comparison of a butt joint with an unbroken piece of the adherend.[8] When electric waves pass from one adherend cylinder (of length 0.5 l cm.) through the adhesive film (of thickness h cm.) into the other adherend (of length 0.5 l cm.), the resonant frequency ν_1 and the width Δ_1 of the resonance band (that is the range of frequencies in which the vibration amplitude is > 0.707 maximum amplitude) are different from those (ν_0 and Δ_0, respectively) of a cylinder, l cm. long and otherwise identical with the adherends. For hard adhesives

$$E = \frac{4\rho}{g_0} h l \nu_0^2 \frac{\nu_1}{\nu_0 - \nu_1} \tag{91}$$

and

$$E_v = \frac{E}{2} \cdot \frac{\Delta_1 - \Delta_0}{\nu_0 - \nu_1} \tag{92}$$

if ρ is the density of the adherend material and g_0 a consistency factor.

Lap Joints

§69. STRESS DISTRIBUTION in lap joints, as long as the deformation is elastic, is influenced by at least three factors. The first is active also when the adherends are absolutely rigid; the second exists because they are extensible, and the third when they are not only extensible but also flexible.

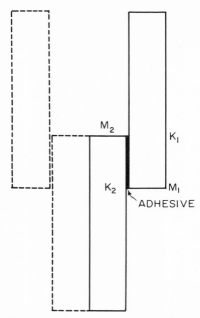

Fig. 64. Geometrical stress concentration in a lap joint.

1. To understand the first factor, supplement a lap joint with its mirror image, as in Fig. 64 in which the real adhint is outlined with a continuous, and the image with an interrupted line. It is clear that the empty rectangle above M_2 must cause a stress concentration analogous to that observed at the corners of a quadratic hole punched in a sheet, §64. As the adhesive, if it perfectly wets the two adherends, will have a boundary with air of the shape of a quarter of a circular cylinder, Fig. 65, the radius of curvature of this boundary will be approximately h_0, if h_0 is the thickness of the adhesive film, while twice the thickness of the adherend, i.e., 2δ would correspond to length l of §64. Thus, if $h_0: 2\delta = 0.014$, the factor of stress concentration at a corner would be about 6, assuming that the deformation of the adherends may be neglected.

2. This deformation, as long as the adherends are not flexible, will tend to lower the above stress concentration but will cause

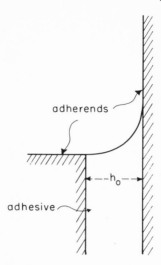

Fɪɢ. 65. The adhesive-air boundary in a lap joint.

another nonuniformity of stress. To make clear that bending is disregarded, we consider the middle member of a *double lap* joint, see Fig. 66. If pull F_0 is applied to this member, force F_0 acts on all cross sections of it above level ab, while evidently tensile force acting on the member at the cd level (i.e., at $z = 0$) is zero. Thus, force F along the axis of z decreases from F_0 to 0 when z decreases from L to 0, L being the length of the overlap. This decrease of F occurs because F is gradually balanced by shearing forces along the adherend–adhesive boundary. Consider a horizontal slice of the middle member, dz cm. thick. The tensile force on its lower boundary is $-F$ and on its upper boundary, $F + (\partial F/\partial z)\, dz$; hence the resultant force is $(\partial F/\partial z)\, dz$. This force is balanced by the two shearing forces along the lines ad and bc; if the shear stress at the given z is τ, each of these forces is $\tau w \cdot dz$, w being the width of the adherend (i.e., normal to the plane of the drawing). Thus, $\partial F/\partial z = 2\tau w$ or, substituting stress f for force F according to equation $F = fw\delta$,

$$\frac{\partial f}{\partial z} = \frac{2\tau}{\delta} \tag{93}$$

δ being the thickness of the middle adherend.

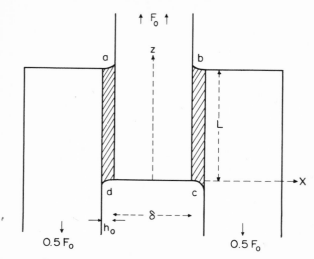

Fig. 66. Differential strain in a double lap joint.

Both $\partial f/\partial z$ and τ can be expressed as functions of the elongation of the middle adherend (and of the adhesive which is supposed to follow all deformations of the bar). If an atom, which was situated z cm. above the cd level before the application of force, is now l cm. above this level, an atom which initially was at $z + dz$ now is at $l + dl$. From Hooke's law (E is Young's modulus of the bar)

$$\frac{\partial(l - z)}{\partial z} = \frac{f}{E} \tag{94}$$

or

$$\frac{\partial^2 l_1}{\partial z^2} = \frac{1}{E} \cdot \frac{\partial f}{\partial z} \tag{95}$$

if l_1 is written for $l - z$. Now we assume that

$$\tau = G_1 l_1 / h_0 \tag{96}$$

G_1 being the modulus of shear of the adhesive and h_0 the thickness of the adhesive film. From (93), (95), and (96), equation

$$\frac{\partial^2 l_1}{\partial z^2} = \frac{2 G_1 l_1}{E \delta h_0} \tag{97}$$

follows. A suitable solution of this equation is (if $f_0 = F_0/w\delta$)

$$l_1 = \frac{f_0}{E}\left(\frac{Eh_0\delta}{2G_1}\right)^{0.5}\frac{e^{\lambda z} - e^{-\lambda z}}{e^{\lambda L} + e^{-\lambda L}}, \qquad \lambda = \left(\frac{2G_1}{E\delta h_0}\right)^{0.5}. \qquad (98)$$

When $z = 0$, then $l_1 = 0$, i.e., there is no stretching of the adherend where, supposedly, no tensile force acts. However, as $f = E(\partial l_1/\partial z)$ from equation (94), f is not equal to zero at $z = 0$. This paradoxical result may be due to the effect considered in §69.1. Because stress concentration exists also when there is no deformation, the variation of the force along the overlap, that is $\partial F/\partial z$ is due not only to the shear stresses along the adherend–adhesive boundary; in other words, equation (94) is not correct. Otherwise equation (98) is reasonable. It satisfies equation (94) at $z = L$. There

$$l_1 = \frac{f_0}{E}\left(\frac{E\delta h_0}{2G_1}\right)^{0.5}\frac{e^{\lambda L} - e^{-\lambda L}}{e^{\lambda L} + e^{-\lambda L}} \approx \frac{f_0}{E}\left(\frac{E\delta h_0}{2G_1}\right)^{0.5}. \qquad (99)$$

Thus the greatest τ, from equation (96), is

$$\tau_{\max} = \left(\frac{G_1\delta}{2Eh_0}\right)^{0.5}f_0. \qquad (100)$$

The average shear stress in the adhesive is

$$\tau_{\mathrm{av}} = \frac{F_0}{wL} = \frac{f_0\delta}{L}. \qquad (101)$$

Hence the greatest stress concentration factor

$$\frac{\tau_{\max}}{\tau_{\mathrm{av}}} = \left(\frac{G_1}{2E\delta h_0}\right)^{0.5}L. \qquad (102)$$

It is present at points a and b of Fig. 66. Equations almost identical with (102) have been derived before.[9, 10]

If rupture occurs when a definite value of $\tau_{\max}$ is reached, equation (100) shows that the external tensile stress f_0 needed to break the adhint is independent of the length L of overlap. Experimentally, breaking stress increases with L; sometimes it is approximately proportional to $L^{0.5}$. This discrepancy manifests another weakness of the theory. The stress concentration described in §69.1 increases with the ratio δ/h_0, while stress concentration factor due to the extensibility of the adherends, see equation (102), is inversely proportional to the root $(\delta h_0)^{0.5}$. When considering these conclusions, the crudeness of the underlying theories should be borne in mind.

The preceding treatment and the final equation (102) can, if at all, be correct only if the adherends and the adhesive are Hookean solids, if contraction normal to the external stress (as in §§67.1 and 67.2) may be neglected, and if no bending of the adherends occurs. This bending is treated in §70.

§70.   Figure 67 illustrates the shape change of a lap joint caused by an external pull; the adhesive is shaded. If the adhint does not break before, it acquires the shape, Fig. 67b, such that the centroid lines of the two adherends far from the overlap are parts of one straight line, and the central point of the adhesive film lies on this line. The overlapping parts of the adherends are each doubly bent, the concave side being away from the adhesive between the center of the latter and the unattached lengths

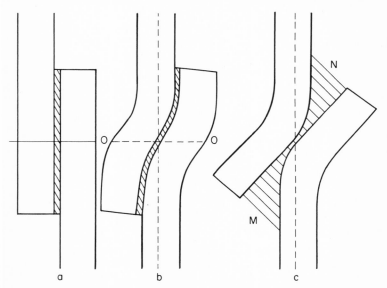

Fig. 67. Deformation of a flexible lap joint.

of each adherend and toward the adhesive near the overlap–air boundaries.

Of the two bends, the second usually will be more dangerous for the joint than the first. When the two adherends meet with their convex sides in contact, the elastic forces in the adherends cause compression of the adhesive film between them, and compressive stresses usually are less destructive for adhesives than are tensile stresses. Strong tensile stresses must be present where the adhesive is situated between a convex surface of one and a concave surface of the other adherend. If the adhesive had no tensile strength, the shape would have been as indicated in Fig. 67c. It is the adhesive that prevents parting of the two solids as shown in the sketch. Thus, near points M and N a tendency to peel is present, and peeling stresses usually cause fracture of lap joints whose adherends are flexible.

A theory, in which this flexibility has been accounted for, exists.[10] When tensile force F_0 is applied to a lap joint of width w and overlap L, not only tension F_0/w but also a moment M_0 and a tension V perpendicular to the plane of the adhesive film act in the adhint. Let σ_f be tensile stress (i.e., in the direction of F_0) in the adherend at the adherend–adhesive boundary, σ_0 be stress in the adhesive perpendicular to the plane of the joint (i.e., the peeling stress as indicated in Fig. 67c), and τ_0 be the shear stress in the adhesive. We are interested in the relations between the greatest values of these stresses and the value of F_0 which, in usual rupture experiments, is increased until the adhint breaks down. These relations depend on the nondimensional ratio $k = 2M_0/F_0\delta$, δ being the thickness of each adherend. This k is equal to 1.00, 0.61, 0.45, and 0.37 when the nondimensional ratio $(L/\delta)(F_0/w\delta E)^{0.5}$ is 0.0, 0.2, 0.4, or 0.6, respectively; E is modulus of elasticity of the adherend material. Thus, in a given adhint, k decreases when F_0 increases; in fact, as a coarse approximation, we may put $k \approx 1 - k_0 F_0^{0.25}$, k_0 being a constant.

The dependence of σ_f, σ_0, and τ_0 on k and, consequently, on F_0 is quite different according to whether the flexibility of the adhint is determined mainly by the adherends or mainly by the adhesive. The first case is observed when $h_0/\delta \ll E_1/E$ and

$h_0/\delta \ll G_1/G$, h_0 being the thickness of the cement layer, E_1 its modulus of elasticity, and G and G_1 the shear moduli of adherend and cement, respectively. For the second case, h_0/δ must be much greater than E_1/E or G_1/G. No approximation is available for the intermediate range in which h_0/δ, E_1/E, and G_1/G have comparable magnitudes; if, for instance, $E = 100\ E_1$, the theory gives no information on lap joints in which ratio δ/h_0 is confined between 10 and 1000. However, some calculations for the intermediate range of $h_0E/\delta E_1$ have been published more recently.[11]

Figure 68 represents stress distribution in the first case. The values of k are plotted along the abscissa from right to left; thus F_0 increases from left to right. The maximum values of

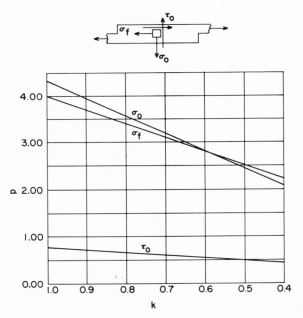

FIG. 68. Stress concentrations in adhints whose flexibility is determined by the adherends. Abscissa: ratio $2M_0/F_0\delta$ plotted from right to left. Ordinate: maximum values of stress concentration factors σ_f/f_0, σ_0/f_0, and τ_0/f_0. From reference 10.

σ_f/f_0, σ_0/f_0, and τ_0/f_0 are indicated along the ordinate; f_0 is defined as $F_0/w\delta$. Thus, for instance, the greatest value of σ_f occurring in a lap joint (for which $h_0/\delta \ll E_1/E$) is 4.0 f_0, i.e., 4.0 times as great as the external stress. When k decreases, i.e., F_0 increases, stress concentration factors σ_f/f_0 etc. decrease because the system is deformed and "adjusts itself" to the external force; as pointed out in §65 also stress concentration factors caused by holes are smaller at greater stresses. The maximum values of the stresses themselves increase with F_0; e.g., F_0 increases fourfold between $k = 0.61$ and $k = 0.45$ while σ_0/f_0 in this range decreases from 2.9 to 2.3 only; thus σ_0 increases in the ratio 9.2 : 2.9.

If E, δ, and F_0 are kept constant, the abscissa of Fig. 68 increases with L (in the direction from left to right). Thus stress concentration factors σ_f/f_0 and so on are smaller the greater L. This is so because the "adjustment" of the glued part is easier the longer this part.

The maximum values of σ_0 and σ_f occur at the two ends of the overlap, i.e., near points M and N of Fig. 67c. When starting from these points we approach plane 00 of the adhint, Fig. 67b, σ_f continues to be a tension stress but σ_0 changes sign and becomes a compression stress, as mentioned in the second paragraph of this section. In some joints, as calculation[11] shows, the cement is slightly compressed for 75% of the length of the overlap and extended only near the overlap ends, but the greatest degree of extension may be ten times the greatest degree of compression.

§71. WHEN $h_0/\delta \gg E_1/E$ and $h_0/\delta \gg G_1/G$, stress concentrations depend on the dimensions of the adhint and on the properties of the adhesive, while none of these factors is of importance in the first case (of $h_0/\delta \ll E_1/E$) except insofar as they affect the value of k. Therefore, instead of σ_0/f_0 as function of k, in Fig. 69 the maximum value of $(\sigma_0/f_0)(L/2\delta)^2$ is plotted along the ordinate as function of $0.5\ L(6E_1/E\delta^3h_0)^{0.25}$ for four different values of parameter k. Consider a system in which L/δ is about 64; then $\sigma_0/f_0 = 0.001$ the ordinate of Fig. 69 and the highest value of σ_0/f_0 indicated is only 0.07.

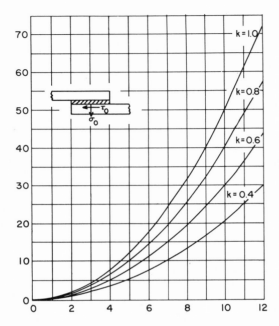

FIG. 69. Stress concentrations in adhints whose flexibility is determined by the adhesive. Abscissa: ratio $0.5\ L(6E_1/E\delta^3h_0)^{0.25}$. Ordinate: maximum values of $(\sigma_0/f_0)(L/2\delta)^2$ From reference 10.

The maximum shear stress in the adhesive (still at $h_0/\delta \gg G_1/G$) for small external forces is

$$\tau_{max} = \frac{f_0\delta}{L}\left[\left(\frac{2G_1L^2}{Eh_0\delta}\right)^{0.5} \coth\left(\frac{2G_1L^2}{Eh_0\delta}\right)^{0.5}\right].$$

In a typical adhint, $(2G_1L^2/Eh_0\delta)^{0.5}$ may be equal to unity; as $\coth 1 = 1.31$, the maximum shearing stress is $1.31\ (f_0\delta/L)$. The average shearing stress, see equation (101), is $f_0\delta/L$; thus the maximum stress concentration factor in this example would be 1.31. The maximum ratio of $\sigma_0L/f_0\delta$ for the example computed in the preceding paragraph would be near 4.4. When $2\ G_1L^2/Eh_0\delta$ is considerably greater than unity, maximum shear stress can be expressed as

$$\tau_{\max} = \left(\frac{2G_1\delta}{Eh_0}\right)^{0.5} f_0, \tag{103}$$

i.e., is twice that given in equation (100). If in addition $h_0 = \delta$, then it is $f_0(2\,G_1/E)^{0.5}$.

If joints of different overlaps L but otherwise of identical dimensions are compared, Fig. 69 becomes one of $\sigma_0 L^2/f_0$ versus L. The effect of L on σ_0/f_0 is difficult to discern from this graph because k itself depends on L but it appears that σ_0/f_0 is less at longer overlaps, as would be expected from a nonmathematical inspection. When rupture occurs in shear, as an increase in L renders equation (103) more nearly valid, the maximum shear stress becomes independent of L; consequently, the maximum concentration of shear stress becomes proportional to L. However, this conclusion must be modified if the external force is not small.

A procedure for predicting the strength of lap joints by combining some theoretical deductions with typical experimental results has been worked out.[12]

§72. ALTHOUGH STRENGTH of lap joints has been measured in very many instances, there appears to exist no systematic comparison between experimental data and the predictions of the above theories. An example of experimental results is shown in Fig. 70 from reference 13. The ordinate of the figure represents the breaking stress $f_m = F_m/w\delta$, F_m being the breaking force of lap joints, in psi (multiply by 0.06895 to obtain stresses in bars) and the abscissa shows $(L/\delta)^2$ on a logarithmic scale. Note that f_m here is not defined as F_m/wL, see §60. One adhesive (a "vinyl-phenolic resin") was used for all adhints. The adherends were a magnesium alloy (FSI-H24), six aluminum alloys (2014, 2024, 7075, 7178, and their variations), and 3 steels (301-¼H, 301-½H, and 17-7PH). It is seen that f_m is independent of L/δ at great overlaps; in this region the adherends break and f_m is the tensile strength of the adherend material; this is, for instance, 180,000 psi for 17-7 steel and 39,000 psi for FSI magnesium. At smaller L/δ values, f_m increases nearly linearly with log (L/δ), that is an increase in L is less effective the greater the ratio L/δ, as it should be according to the theory, see §§70 and 76. Thus, for

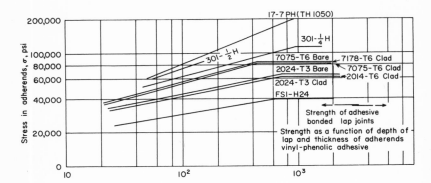

FIG. 70. Experimental rupture stress and dimensions of lap joints. Abscissa: $\log (L/\delta)^2$. Ordinate: breaking stress in psi. One adhesive and seven different metallic adherends. From reference 13.

magnesium, an increase of L/δ from 40 to 100 raises f_m from 28,200 to 30,500 psi, while an increase from 200 to 260 causes a rise of f_m from 34,000 to only 35,800 psi.

The f_m of Fig. 70 is greater the greater the tensile strength and the modulus of elasticity of the metal. This also is in agreement with the theory. It is clear from equation (102) and §71 that products $E\delta$ rather than the values of δ itself should be compared when different adherends are studied. Thus f_m should be represented as a function of $(L/\delta E)^2$ rather than of $(L/\delta)^2$. The E of steel 17-7 is about 4.4 times that of magnesium FSI. As $4.4^2 \approx 19$, ratio $(L/\delta)^2 = 20$ for steel is equivalent to ratio $(L/\delta)^2 = 20 \times 19 = 380$ for magnesium; and indeed extrapolation of the uppermost line to $(L/\delta)^2 = 20$ leads to a f_m of about 40,000 psi, i.e., only a few per cents greater than f_m of FSI at $(L/\delta)^2 = 380$.

Peeling, see §70, which so markedly lowers f_m can be reduced not only by making both adherends stiff but also by combining a thin plate with a thick block, as indicated in Figs. 71 and 72. Breaking stress again is the ordinate, but this time L/δ is plotted on the abscissa; δ is the thickness of the plate, not of the block. In the experiments of Fig. 71, upper line, two thin plates of aluminum alloy 7075 were glued to a block of an identical alloy,

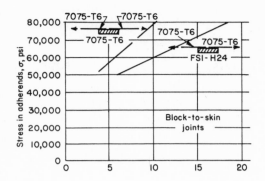

FIG. 71. Rupture stress of stiffened lap joints. Abscissa: L/δ. Ordinate: breaking stress in psi. From reference 13.

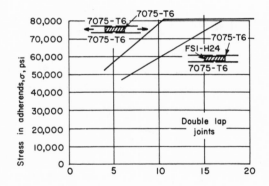

FIG. 72. Rupture stress of double lap joints. Abscissa: L/δ. Ordinate: breaking stress in psi. From reference 13.

and pull was applied to the plates. The lower line is for two aluminum alloy plates glued to a magnesium block. Figure 72 refers to double lap joints, the medium adherend being a block; the composition of the adherends is marked as in Fig. 71. Naturally, the highest breaking stress attained in all instances was equal to the tensile strength of the 7075 alloy. However, the ratio L/δ at which the greatest stress was reached was different for different blocks and, above all, different from the L/δ value at which tensile strength is reached in ordinary lap joints, see Fig. 70. As this figure shows, for the 7075 alloy $(L/\delta)^2$ was about 420, i.e., L/δ was about 20 when f_m became independent of L/δ. For lap joints supported by thick blocks, see Figs. 71 and 72, the kink was observed at L/δ values as low as 10 or 11. In other words, the joint ceased to be the weakest region of the system at overlaps which for supported lap joints were only half as long as for unsupported adhints.

Additional experimental data on the relative strength of single and double lap joints are shown in Fig. 73.[14] The adherends were 99.5% aluminum (left), an Al-Mg-Mn alloy, and an Al-Cu-Mg alloy (right). Their yield stresses (in kg.-wt./mm.², multiply by 98.1 to obtain them in bars) are plotted along the abscissa, and f_m (kg.-wt./mm.²) along the ordinate. The lower shaded strip is for single, and the upper, for double lap joints. The f_m is defined as force F_m divided by the glued area, §60, but

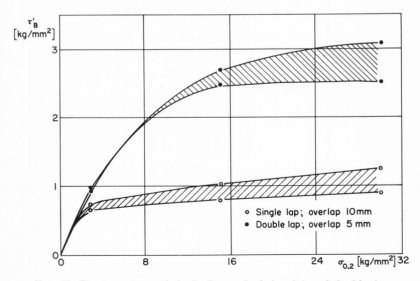

FIG. 73. Rupture stress of single (lower shaded strip) and double (upper shaded strip) lap joints. Abscissa: yield stress of the adherend metal in kg wt./mm.². Ordinate: breaking stress in kg. wt./mm.² From reference 14.

it is not clear whether the glued area of the double lap system was taken as equal to, or twice as great as, that of the single lap assembly; the overlap L was 1.0 or 0.5 cm. and the width w was 2.5 cm.

The importance of the stress concentration near the two ends of the overlap in a single lap joint could be demonstrated in a striking manner.[15] Lap joints with an overlap length of 2.5 cm. failed at loads near 3000 lb. (i.e., 1.335×10^9 dynes). When adhints were made in which the 2.5 cm. long overlap was only half-filled with the adhesive, namely 0.625 cm. band of adhesive– 1.25 cm. unfilled center of the overlap–0.625 cm. long band of adhesive, breaking force was 2500 lb. (1.11×10^9 dynes). Thus removal of the middle half of the adhesive film lowered the resistance of the adhint by only 20%.

§73. A lap joint can be subjected to bending rather than to pull. Stresses occurring in this operation have been calculated and also measured by the photoelasticity technique.[16] Figure 74 indicates the system. "Tab" is a thin plate (of thickness h_1) glued or brazed to a thicker "base bar" (of thickness h_2), and the thickness of the adhesive film ("braze") is h_b. Stress σ_{max} is that stress which would exist in the uppermost fibers of the base if its free end (to the right) was bent down in the absence of braze and tab; because braze and tab are there, the actual maximum stress at the boundary between base, braze, and air is $k\sigma_{max}$. Letter p indicates the major principal stress in the braze, and ratio p/σ_{max} is a measure of the stress concentration achieved in the joint. Figure 75 presents calculated and experimental values of this ratio (along the ordinate) as functions of the adhesive thickness h_b (along the abscissa). The upper two curves are valid for relatively thick tabs ($h_1 = 0.20$ cm., $h_2 = 0.63$ cm., i.e., $h_1{:}h_2 \approx 0.32$); for the middle two curves ratio $h_1{:}h_2$ is 0.16, and for the lower pair, $h_1{:}h_2 = 0.08$. Thus, a stress concentration factor of almost five is reached when $h_1{:}h_2$ is not too small and when $h_b{:}h_2$ is very small (in our instance, 0.004). When h_b is infinitely small compared with h_1 and h_2, stress concentration is analogous to that referred to in §69.1 and the stress concentration factor is infinitely great if the tab and the base bar form an

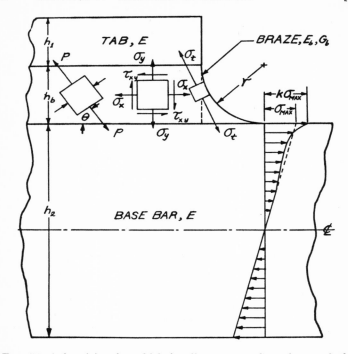

FIG. 74. A lap joint for which bending stresses have been calculated. From reference 16.

exact right angle, i.e., if the radius of curvature (r in Fig. 74) is zero.

The values of σ_x, σ_y, and τ_{xy} decrease when the distance from the "fillet" (whose radius of curvature is r) increases, i.e., when we move to the left in the braze layer of Fig. 74. Figure 76 demonstrates this behavior of σ_y/σ_{max} for the interface of base bar and braze. In these tests, h_1 was 0.10, $h_2 = 0.63$, and $h_b = 0.025$ cm. It is seen that the effect of the edge is small when the distance from the edge exceeds 0.05 cm., i.e., 2 h_b.

§74.   THE STRENGTH of a lap joint can be raised by making the angle between the plane of the adhesive film and the axis of the adherends less than 90°, that is by using scarf joints. Figure 77 represents such an adhint; φ is the "scarf angle", δ the thick-

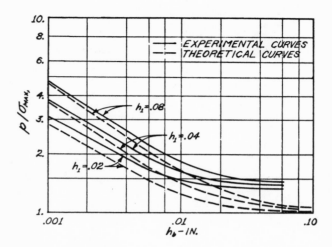

Fig. 75. Stress concentration in a bent lap joint. Abscissa: thickness of the adhesive film in inches. Ordinate: ratio p/σ_{max}. From reference 16.

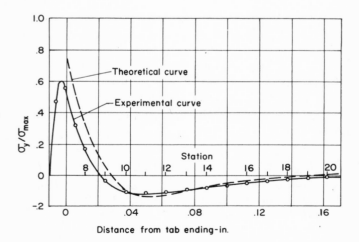

Fig. 76. Stress concentrations at the interface between adherend and adhesive. Abscissa: distance from the air-adhesive-adherend line. Ordinate: σ_y/σ_{max}. From reference 16.

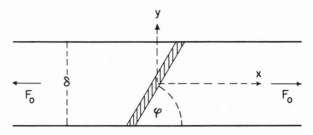

Fig. 77. A scarf joint; φ is the scarf angle.

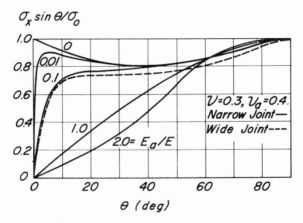

Fig. 78. Breaking stress in scarf joints, rupture occurring in tension. Abscissa: scarf angle. Ordinate: $f_m \sin \varphi / \sigma_m$. From reference 17.

ness of the adherend bar, and F_0 is the external force; the adhesive film is shaded.

The main results of a theory[17] of scarved joints are shown in Figs. 78 and 79.

In calculating the data on which Fig. 78 is based it was assumed that rupture occurred as soon as tensile stress at any point in the adhesive exceeded a value σ_m. The ordinate of the figure represents ratio $f_m \sin \varphi / \sigma_m$, if f_m is the breaking stress, i.e., the maximum value of F_m divided by $w\delta$; w is again the width of the adherend bar. The scarf angle is plotted along the abscissa. Note that all lines reach the value of unity at $\varphi = 90°$,

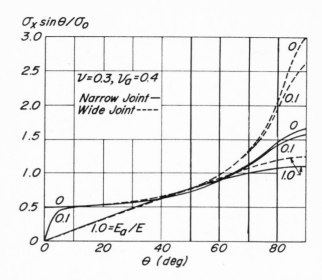

FIG. 79. Breaking stress in scarf joints, rupture occurring in shear. Abscissa: scarf angle. Ordinate: $f_m \sin \varphi / 2\tau_{max}$. From reference 17.

i.e., for a butt joint. This observation characterizes the range of validity of the theory; evidently, the theory neglects the stress concentrations discussed in §67. Thus it may be argued that it deals only with the difference between butt and scarf joints without delving into the absolute values of strength in either system; in other words, if σ_m is the fracture stress of a butt joint (rather than the maximum local stress), the breaking stress f_m of an analogous scarf joint would be given by Fig. 78.

The numerical data of Fig. 78 are valid if Poisson's ratio is 0.3 for the adherend and 0.4 for the adhesive. The numbers marked at the curves signify the ratio E_1/E, E_1 and E being the moduli of elasticity of adhesive and adherend, respectively. The discontinuous curve is computed for a wide joint having $E_1/E = 0.1$, while the continuous curves are for narrow joints. Since usual values of E_1/E are confined between 0.01 and 0.1 and the usual scarf angles are greater than 10° and smaller than 80°, Fig. 78 demonstrates that the effect of φ on $f_m \sin \varphi$ is not very great. The f_m itself is, for $E_1/E = 0.1$, about four times as great at $\varphi = 10°$ as at $80°$.

When the adhesive ruptures in shear rather than in tension, Fig. 79 rather than Fig. 78 should be consulted. A crack is assumed to appear as soon as shear stress anywhere in the adhesive exceeds a value equal to τ_{max}. The ordinate of Fig. 79 is f_m sin $\varphi/2\tau_{max}$, and the abscissa again is φ. The continuous curves are for narrow, and the discontinuous for wide adhints. The value of f_m sin φ in the most important range of angles φ, i.e., between $\varphi = 20°$ and $\varphi = 70°$, evidently little depends on E_1/E and almost linearly increases with φ. If f_m were simply proportional to the area of the adhesive film, f_m sin φ were independent of φ.

Because the dependence of f_m on φ is different in Fig. 78 and Fig. 79, it is possible to decide whether tensile or shear failure caused the breakdown of a scarf joint by comparing the experimental curve of "f_m versus φ" with the two theoretical curves. In Fig. 80 such an experimental curve is shown. The experiments have been performed by Hartman[18] but the data are taken from reference 17. The five vertical lines indicate the ranges of the experimental breaking stresses f_m of adhints made of duraluminum plates and a commercial poly(vinyl acetate) adhesive at different scarf angles plotted along the abscissa. The circles are the mean values of f_m sin φ. As the curve connecting these is more similar to those of Fig. 78 than to those of Fig. 79, we conclude that the adhesive probably failed in tension, not in shear.

§75.   A TYPE INTERMEDIATE between an ordinary lap joint and a scarf joint has recently been suggested and studied by the photoelasticity method.[19] It is indicated in Fig. 81. When pull is applied in the direction of the arrows, point a of the upper adherend is pressed toward point b of the lower adherend; thus the peeling effect depicted in Fig. 67c should not occur. Photoelastic observations confirmed this conclusion. It is still unknown how the strength of these scarf-lap joints compares with that of ordinary lap and ordinary scarf adhints. The fringe pattern of an ordinary lap joint greatly depended on the direction of the external force, see Fig. 82, but the dependence of the breaking stress on angle φ has not been determined.

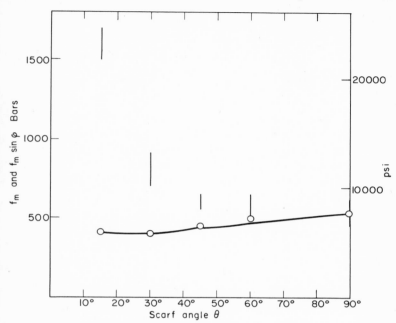

Fig. 80. Experimental dependence of breaking stress on scarf angle. Abscissa: scarf angle. Ordinate: breaking stress f_m (vertical lines) and $f_m \sin \varphi$ (circles) in bars and psi. Data of reference 18.

§76.   A CYLINDRICAL LAP JOINT is a simpler system than the flat lap joints discussed in §§69 to 73. Figure 83 shows the notations used. The annular space between two hollow circular cylinders, each of thickness δ, is filled with an adhesive (of thickness h_0) along overlap L. The outside diameter of the inner tube is $2a - h_0$, and the inside diameter of the outer tube is $2a + h_0$. Pull F_0 is applied in the direction of the black arrows; thus the mean shear stress in the adhesive is $F_0/2\pi aL$.

The greatest shear stress τ_{max} and the greatest normal stress σ_{max} in the adhesive occur along the 3-phase line in which the inner tube, the cement, and air meet.[20] Thus, contrary to flat lap joints, the two adherends are not interchangeable even if their thicknesses are equal. Because the cross-sectional area (normal to the cylinder axis) of the inner tube $[\pi(2a\delta - \delta^2 - h_0\delta)]$

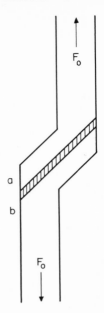

FIG. 81. A modified scarf joint.

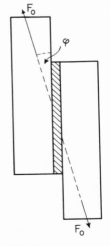

FIG. 82. A lap joint stressed at an acute angle.

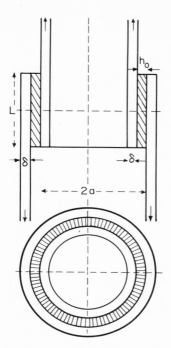

FIG. 83. A cylindrical lap joint.

is smaller than that of the outer tube $[\pi(2a\delta + \delta^2 + h_0\delta)]$, the stress in the former is greater, its deformation also is greater, and finally the stress concentration at its surface is greater than at the end of the wider tube.

Figure 84 shows the dependence of $2\pi aL\tau_{max}/F_0$ (i.e., of the stress concentration factor) plotted along the ordinate as a function of the "rigidity parameter" $h_0E/E_1\delta$ along the abscissa; E and E_1 are the moduli of elasticity of adherend and adhesive, respectively. At each curve the ratio $R = \delta/2a$ and (in parentheses) the ratio L/δ are marked; thus the top curve is calculated for $2a = 100\delta$ and $L = 10\delta$. In the calculations it is assumed that Poisson's ratios are 0.3 for all materials and that $E_1 = (8/3)G_1$, G_1 being the shear modulus of the adhesive. It is seen that the stress concentration factor for shear rarely exceeds two, i.e., as

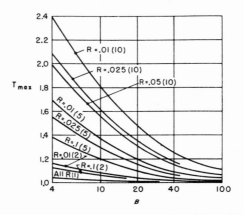

FIG. 84. Shear stress concentration in tubular lap joints. Abscissa: rigidity parameter $h_0E/E_1\delta$. Ordinate: stress concentration factor $2\pi aL\tau_{max}/F_0$. From reference 20.

a rule is smaller than those observed in flat lap joints; greater factors would be attained at smaller "rigidity parameters" but the theory is not likely to be even approximately correct when $h_0/\delta < 4E_1/E$.

Figure 85 represents analogous calculations for the tensile stress; ratio $2\pi aL\sigma_{max}/F_0$ is plotted along the ordinate while the abscissa again is $h_0E/E_1\delta$. The two graphs for τ_{max} and σ_{max} obviously are very similar.

In Fig. 86 the ratio of "external stress at failure" (equal to $F_m/2\pi a\delta$, if F_m is the load causing rupute) to the largest value (σ_0) of the principal tensile stress is shown; it is postulated that rupture starts as soon as σ_0 exceeds a minimum value characteristic for the adhesive material. The abscissa represents the ratio of overlap length to adherend thickness, i.e., L/δ. Figure 86a is calculated for a relatively stiff adhesive film (having $h_0E/E_1\delta$ equal to 4) while Fig. 86b is valid for a more flexible adhint (with $h_0E/E_1\delta$ equal to 100). If no stress concentration took place in the joint, F_m and $F_m/2\pi a\delta\sigma_0$ would increase linearly with the length L of the overlap; this hypothetical condition is shown by the straight lines marked $\beta = \infty$. The lines marked $R = 0.10$ and $R = 0.01$ are calculated for tubular joints whose

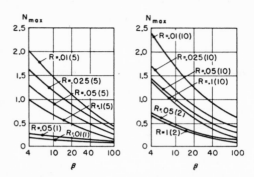

Fig. 85. Tensile stress concentration in tubular lap joints. Abscissa: rigidity parameter $h_0E/E_1\delta$. Ordinate: stress concentration factor $2\pi aL\sigma_{max}/F_0$. From reference 20.

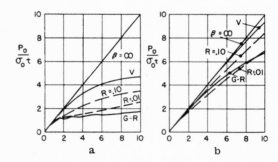

Fig. 86. Theoretical relation between breaking stress and adhint dimensions in flat and tubular lap joints. Abscissa: L/δ. Ordinate: $F_m/2\pi a\delta\sigma_0$. Ratio $h_0E/E_1\delta$ is 4 for Fig. 86a and 100 for Fig. 86b. From reference 20.

ratios $\delta/2a$ are 0.10 and 0.01, respectively; it is manifest that the strength of the adhint is not proportional to L; when $h_0E/E_1\delta = 4$, F_m increases roughly as $L^{0.5}$ and when $h_0E/E_1\delta = 100$, F_m is approximately proportional to $L^{0.8}$ to $L^{0.9}$. For comparison, two other curves, both for flat lap joints, are drawn. That marked V indicates the dependence of F_m on L according to equation (100) and that marked $G - R$ is drawn in agreement with the theory of §70. Figure 86 is a particularly clear summary of present theoretical predictions for the relation between strength and overlap in lap joints.

Peeling

§77. Peeling has been mentioned as taking place in the
rupture of lap joints by a tensile force, §70. However, usual
peeling tests are different and can be typified by Fig. 87. A

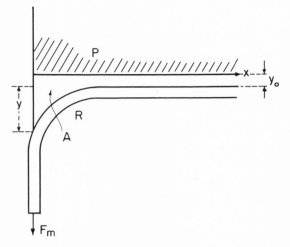

Fig. 87. A peeling test.

flexible ribbon of width w is attached to a rigid plate by a cement;
when a sufficiently great force F_m is applied to the free end of the
ribbon, the adhesive film rips at the bend of the ribbon, and the
"knee" gradually travels to the right. The mechanism of this
operation has been studied by Spies[21] but the treatment in this
monograph follows a later, simplified theory.[22]

It is postulated that both ribbon and adhesive are Hookean
solids and that shear stresses in the adhesive are negligible, that
is each fiber or column of the adhesive reaching from the plate to
the ribbon is extended (when ribbon curves) in the direction of
the applied force without any interference by the neighboring
fibers or columns. Tearing occurs when the extension of the column nearest to the load (i.e., at the left-hand end of the adhesive
film in Fig. 87) reaches the greatest value possible in the adhesive.

Thus, if the total relative elongation of the adhesive substance is ϵ_m and the initial thickness of the adhesive film is h_0, film starts ripping when the fiber nearest to the load acquires the length of $(1 + \epsilon_m)h_0$.

For a Hookean solid

$$\epsilon_m = \frac{\sigma_m}{E_1} \tag{104}$$

σ_m being the tensile strength and E_1 the modulus of elasticity of the cement.

To find the value of F_m at which the strain (or relative elongation) ϵ attains, at any point of the adhesive film, its maximum value equal to ϵ_m, we consider the forces acting on any cross section of the ribbon. If, at any value of x, Fig. 87, the thickness of the adhesive is $h_0 + y$, and if (as for Hookean solids) extension y implies stress $(y/h_0)E_1$, then a strip of the ribbon, dx cm. long and w cm. deep (w is perpendicular to the plane of the sketch) is pulled up with the force $(y/h_0)E_1w \cdot dx$. Hence[23]

$$\frac{d^4y}{dx^4} = -\frac{12E_1y}{E\delta^3h_0}, \tag{105}$$

E and δ are again the modulus of elasticity and the thickness of the ribbon. If we abbreviate $3\,E_1/E\delta^3h_0$ as n^4, we obtain

$$\frac{d^4y}{dx^4} = -4n^4y \tag{106}$$

which is satisfied, for instance, by setting

$$y = Ae^{-nx}\cos nx. \tag{107}$$

This equation contains only one adjustable constant, namely A. Therefore it can be valid only if either a force or a moment, not both a force and a moment, is applied to the free end of the ribbon. We consider here the instance of a force.

This force (F_0) is compensated by the sum of the forces $(y/h_0)E_1w \cdot dx$, see preceding paragraph. Thus,

$$F_0 = \frac{E_1wA}{h_0}\int_0^l e^{-nx}\cos nx\ dx = \frac{E_1wA}{2nh_0} \tag{108}$$
$$(e^{-nl}\sin nl - e^{-nl}\cos nl + 1)$$

if l is the length of the glued part of the ribbon. For this equation to be valid, l must be long, i.e., nl must be considerably greater than unity; then the term e^{-nl} (sin nl − cos nl) may be neglected in comparison with unity. Thus

$$F_0 = \frac{E_1 wA}{2nh_0} \text{ and } A = \frac{2nh_0 F_0}{E_1 w}. \tag{109}$$

At $x = 0$, from (107) and (109), $y = 2 \, nh_0 F_0 / E_1 w$. Rupture starts when this y reaches the value of $\epsilon_m h_0$. Thus, see equation (104), $F_m = w\sigma_m / 2 \, n$ or

$$F_m = \frac{1}{2 \times 3^{0.25}} w\sigma_m \left(\frac{E\delta^3 h_0}{E_1} \right)^{0.25} = 0.3799 \, w\sigma_m (E/E_1)^{0.25} \delta^{0.75} h_0^{0.25}. \tag{110}$$

Comparison of equation (110) with the zero-order approximation for butt joints, namely

$$F_m = wl\sigma_m \tag{111}$$

is instructive. The numerical value of $0.3799 \, (E/E_1)^{0.25}$ usually is of the order of unity. Thus, in peeling, $F_m \approx w\delta^{0.75} h_0^{0.25} \sigma_m$. If $\delta = h_0$, we have simply

$$F_m \approx wh_0\sigma_m. \tag{112}$$

Thus in tensile tests the external force is equal to σ_m multiplied with the greatest cross section of the adhesive film (namely length × width), while in peeling F_m is equal to σ_m multiplied with the smallest cross section (i.e., width × thickness); it is clear that peeling must be much easier than pulling, as it indeed is.

§78.   TAKE NOW the case such that the adherend still is a Hookean solid while the stress–strain curve of the adhesive may be approximated as

$$\sigma = e_1\epsilon^m \tag{113}$$

(ϵ^m should not be confused with ϵ_m !); σ = stress, ϵ = strain, e_1 is a material constant, and m is an exponent (another material constant) which may have any value less than unity. Then, instead of (105), equation

$$\frac{d^4y}{dx^4} = -\frac{12e_1y^m}{E\delta^3h_0{}^m} \tag{114}$$

results. It can be satisfied, for instance, by setting

$$y = Ax^j, \tag{115}$$

the constants A and j to be derived from the boundary conditions. If the reasoning of the preceding section is repeated for this case, the following expression[24] for the stripping force F_m is arrived at

$$F_m = \left[\frac{(3+m)(2+2m)}{3(1+3m)^3}\right]^{0.25} \frac{w\sigma_m{}^{(3m+1)/4m}E^{0.25}\delta^{0.75}h_0{}^{0.25}}{e_1{}^{1/4m}}. \tag{116}$$

Perhaps the most striking peculiarity of this expression is that F_m is not proportional to σ_m, as in equation (110), but rises with σ_m more rapidly than σ_m itself. For instance, when $m = 0.5$,

$$F_m = 0.688w\sigma_m{}^{1.25}E^{0.25}\delta^{0.75}h_0{}^{0.25}/e_1{}^{0.5} \tag{117}$$

and increases in the ratio 2.38:1 when σ_m increases twofold. If two adhesives having identical values of σ_m are compared, that material whose ϵ_m is smaller usually will be easier to strip off than the cement of a higher ϵ_m; this is understandable because the area of the adhesive film in which this is significantly stretched by the external force is greater the greater ϵ_m.

§79. EQUATIONS (110) and (116), in spite of their outward complexity, are as crude an approximation as equation (111) is. They disregard all stress concentrations analogous to those outlined in §§67 to 76 for butt and lap joints. This defect makes itself felt when the theoretical predictions are tested by experiment.

Such a test was carried out [24] with glass as the plate material, aluminum and nickel as ribbon materials, and various polyethylenes (purified, §48) and a poly(vinyl acetate) as the adhesive. The discrepancy between theory and experiment is illustrated in Table IX.

Table IX

Stripping Force (for 1 cm. Width) of Aluminum–Polyethylene–
Glass Adhints

Polyethylene	F_m kilo dynes experimental	F_m (kilo dynes) calculated from Eq. (110)	from Eq. (117)
Epolene	100	579	
Epolene 1 + Marlex 0.67	250	749	
Epolene 1 + Marlex 1.5	420	732	1430
Epolene 1 + Marlex 3.0	740		2720

Equation (110) was used to calculate F_m for the low-molecular polyethylene known as Epolene and for a mixture of this substance with 0.67 part of Marlex (a high-molecular polyethylene) because these hydrocarbons behaved as near-Hookean solids. The other two mixtures approximately satisfied equation (113) with $m = 0.5$; the F_m of one of them was calculated also from equation (110) to illustrate the numerical difference between the two approximations.

The ratio of calculated to experimental F_m varied between 3 and almost 6 and, apparently, little depended on the rigidity or flexibility of the cement. However, the dependence of F_m on ribbon width w was different according to whether the adhesive was a near-Hookean solid or had $m \approx 0.5$. Figure 88 summarizes the experimental results; its ordinate is stripping force F_m (in kilodynes) and its abscissa is w in cm. The F_m of brittle solids (the two lower lines) is proportional to w, as predicted by equations (110) and (116) and as often is assumed without any proof, but F_m for the elastoplastic mixture of Epolene 1 + Marlex 3 is not; for this polymer an equation

$$F_m = 1.4 \times 10^5 + 3.5 \times 10^5 \, w \text{ dynes} \tag{118}$$

(if w is in cm.) seems to emerge. The author accounts for this strange relation in the following manner.

When the adhesive is extended parallel to the y coordinate, see Fig. 87, it must contract (because Poisson's ratio is not zero) in the direction perpendicular to x and y, which may be designated as z, see Fig. 89. Thus, at the two extremities of the width of the adhesive film (this width is parallel to z) stress concentrations must appear, analogous to those depicted in Fig. 57.

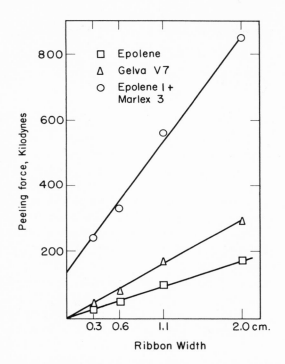

FIG. 88. Experimental dependence of peeling force F_m on ribbon width w. Abscissa: w in cm. Ordinate: F_m in kilodynes. Upper line: an elastoplastic adhesive. Lower lines: brittle adhesives. Data of reference 24.

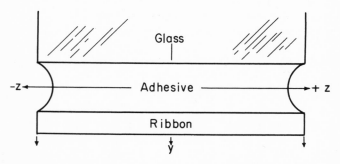

FIG. 89. Lateral contraction of the adhesive during peeling.

Let that part of the width which is subjected to concentrated stresses be w_1 and the average tension in it be ζ_1; and let ζ_0 be the average (nearly constant) tension acting on the rest of the width, that is on $w - w_1$. Evidently, $\zeta_1 > \zeta_0$ and $w \gg w_1$. The total force F_m can thus be written as a sum: $F_m = \zeta_1 w_1 + \zeta_0(w - w_1)$ or

$$F_m = \zeta_0 w + (\zeta_1 - \zeta_0)w_1. \tag{119}$$

Comparing (119) with (118), we conclude that $(\zeta_1 - \zeta_0)w_1$ was 1.4×10^5 dynes and ζ_0 was 3.5×10^5 dynes/cm. The length w_1 must be, according to Saint-Vénant's principle (see also §73), for both ends of the width together, about twice the thickness of the adhesive film. This was 0.024 cm. Assume $w_1 = 0.05$ cm. Then $\zeta_1 - \zeta_0 = 28 \times 10^5$ dynes/cm. and $\zeta_1 = 31.5 \times 10^5$ dynes/cm. The force on 1 cm. thus would be 3150 kilodynes, i.e., nearly equal to the theoretical value listed in Table IX.

That F_m sometimes is not proportional to w, was observed also in other experiments.[25]

§80. SINCE, see the two lower lines of Fig. 88, the F_m of brittle cements is proportional to w, the most dangerous stress concentration in these adhints is not likely to be situated at the extremities of the width. Its location seems to be, instead, at the "knee" of the ribbon. If the ribbon material were a Hookean solid, the longitudinal stress in its external fibers (i.e., at the boundary with the adhesive) would be $\delta E/2R$, R being the radius of curvature of the ribbon at the bend. This R usually was near 0.1 cm. The stress calculated in this manner was markedly greater than the yield stress of the metal. Thus, the ribbon was plastically deformed at the "knee"; this was confirmed also by the fact that the ribbon did not straighten itself on removal of the external load. If the ribbon length at the knee increased, say, by $100\epsilon\%$ of its original length, the adhesive in contact with the ribbon also should have extended in the ratio $(1 + \epsilon) : 1$; if, however, the total relative elongation of the brittle adhesive was less than ϵ, the adhesive must have cracked.

This conclusion was substantiated by two observations. (a) While in the adhints containing flexible cements comparable

amounts of adhesive remained on both the rigid plate and the
ribbon, the separation in the brittle cements took place so near
the ribbon that the thickness of the film remaining on the ribbon
could not always be measured by mechanical means; apparently
it did not exceed a few microns. Thus, rupture really originated
in the vicinity of the ribbon. It could be shown by special experiments that this was not due to the presence of a weak boundary layer.

(b) If failure of the adhesive in contact with the ribbon really
was due to the excessive stretching of the latter, it ought to
be possible to reproduce this effect by stretching the ribbon without peeling and then applying stripping force. Figure 90 illustrates the technique used. Adhints of the usual shape were
prepared and weights W were applied to the ribbons so as to
extend them past the yield point without increasing the distance between plate and ribbon; the angle α was between 1°
and 5°. Then the weights were removed, the plates placed in
horizontal position, and the ribbons were stripped off with a

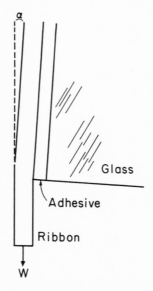

Fig. 90. Stretching a ribbon without peeling.

force equal to about 25% of the force needed to peel an un-
damaged adhint. It was found that 0.2 to 0.7 cm. could be
stripped off in this manner; thus, stretching the ribbon parallel
to itself must have caused cracking of the cement along 0.2–
0.7 cm. length. Similar stretching of ribbons glued to glass with
a flexible adhesive had no effect on the minimum peeling force
as determined in a subsequent experiment.

It may be worth pointing out here, in reference to §59.2, that
in a group of three materials of which one was nonpolar and
flexible, another nonpolar and brittle, and the third polar and
brittle, the two last named, not the two first-named behaved
in similar manner, see Fig. 88. The degree of brittleness, not the
degree of polarity was important.

§81.   THE DISCUSSION of §§77–80 deals with peeling at a
right angle; the direction of the external force F_m was perpendicular to the adhesive–plate interface. Stripping can be achieved
also at any other angle greater than 0° and equal to, or smaller
than, 180°. When peeling angle φ, see Fig. 91, is small, the cement
is sheared in addition to being extended normally to the above
interface. If stripping starts when force F_m acts at angle φ, then
the work W of stripping is[26]

$$W = F_m l (1 - \cos \varphi) \tag{120}$$

if l is the length of the stripped area. Equation (120) is readily

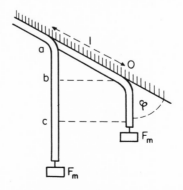

FIG. 91. Peeling at an acute angle φ.

proved on hand of Fig. 91. A material particle which initially was at the 3-phase line, after length l has been stripped off, now is in position c. Thus, $\overline{ac} = l$. But the load descended only by the distance $\overline{bc} = \overline{ac} - \overline{ab} = l - l \cdot \cos \varphi$. Thus, the work done by the load is given by equation (120). When $\varphi = 90°$ as assumed in Section 77,

$$W = F_m l. \tag{121}$$

When $\varphi = 180°$, $W = 2\,F_m l$. If the *work* of peeling is a fundamental quantity independent of φ, then it would follow from equation (120) that peeling *force* is inversely proportional to $(1 - \cos \varphi)$.

Experimental results concerning the relation between F_m and φ are meager. Figure 92 is based on the data[27] obtained by

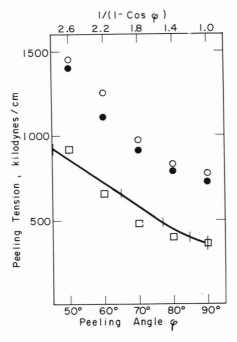

FIG. 92. Experimental relation between peeling tension F_m/w and peeling angle φ. Abscissa (bottom) is φ; abscissa (top) is $1/(1 - \cos \varphi)$. Ordinate: F_m/w in kilodynes/cm. A poly(vinyl acetate) adhesive. Data of reference 27.

peeling a poly(vinyl acetate) film reinforced with a silk fabric from a glass plate. Peeling tension ($= F_m/w$) in kilodynes/cm. is plotted along the ordinate. The lower scale of the abscissa represents peeling angle φ, and the upper scale is $1/(1 - \cos \varphi)$. For white circles, black circles, and squares the bottom scale is valid; the amount of plasticizer (tricresyl phosphate) in the film was 20, 40, and 60 g. for 100 g. resin, respectively, for these three sets of data. The vertical lines and the curve connecting them refer to the upper scale and the 60 : 100 mixture; the curves for the other two mixtures would be almost parallel to that shown. The deviation of the curve from a straight line is not very serious; thus in the instance of plasticized poly(vinyl acetate) the work of peeling was almost independent of peeling angle.

The stripping tension at $\varphi = 45°$ was always greater than that at $\varphi = 90°$ also when an epoxy resin cross-linked with phthalic anhydride or a diamine was the adhesive and an aluminum alloy the adherend, see Fig. 104 in §95. Stripping tension at $\varphi = 180°$ was, with different adhesives, either greater or smaller than, or indistinguishable from, that at $\varphi = 90°$. The effects were complicated by the buckling of the metal ribbon caused by the shrinkage of the adhesive.[28]

REFERENCES

1. Timoshenko, S., *Phil. Mag.* [6] **47**, 1095 (1924).
2. Kobatake, Y., and Inoue, Y., *Appl. Sci. Research* **A7**, 100 (1958).
3. Mylonas, C., *Proc. Soc. Exptl. Stress Anal.* **12**, No. 2, 129 (1955).
4. Hill, R., "The Mathematical Theory of Plasticity," p. 233. Oxford Univ. Press, London and New York, 1950.
5. Shield, R. T., *Quart. Appl. Math.* **15**, 139 (1957).
6. Meyerhof, G. G., and Chaplin, T. K., *Brit. J. Appl. Phys.* **4**, 20 (1953).
7. Norris, C. B., James, W. L., and Drow, J. T., *Am. Soc. Testing Materials Bull.* **218**, 40 (1956).
8. Dietz, A. G. H., Closmann, P. J., Kavanagh, G. M:, and Rossen, J. N., *Proc. Am. Soc. Testing Materials* **50**, 1414 (1950).
9. Volkersen, O., *Luftfahrt-Forschung* **15**, 41 (1938).
10. Goland, M., and Reissner, E., *J. Appl. Mech.* **11**, 17 (1944).
11. Sherrer, R. E., *U.S. Dept. Agr., Forest Serv. Forest Prods. Lab. Rept.* **1864** (1957).
12. Tombach, H., *Machine Design* **29**, No. 7, 113 (1957).

13. Sheridan, M. L., and Merriman, H. R., *Am. Soc. Testing Materials Spec. Tech. Bull. No.* **201**, 33 (1957).
14. Kaliske, G., *Aluminium* **31**, 275 (1955).
15. Koehn, G. W., *in* "Adhesion and Adhesives. Fundamentals and Practice," p. 120. Wiley, New York, 1954.
16. Cornell, R. W., *J. Appl. Mech.* **20**, 355 (1953).
17. Lubkin, J. L., *J. Appl. Mech.* **24**, 255 (1957).
18. Hartman, A., *Neth. Luchtvaartlabor. Rept. No.* M1275 (1948).
19. McLaren, A. S., and MacInnes, I., *Brit. J. Appl. Phys.* **9**, 72 (1958).
20. Lubkin, J. L., and Reissner, E., *Trans. Am. Soc. Mech. Engrs.* **78**, 1213 (1956).
21. Spies, J., *Aircraft Eng.* **25**, No. 289, 64 (1953).
22. Bikerman, J. J., *J. Appl. Phys.* **28**, 1484 (1957).
23. Hetényi, M., "Beams on Elastic Foundation." Univ. of Michigan Press, Ann Arbor, Michigan, 1946.
24. Bikerman, J. J., *J. Appl. Polymer Sci.* **2**, 216 (1959).
25. Hammond, G. L., and Moakes, R. C. W., *Trans. Inst. Rubber Ind.* **25**, 172 (1949).
26. Deryagin, B. V., and Krotova, N. A., "Adgeziya," p. 55. Acad. sci. U.S.S.R., Moscow, 1949.
27. Inoue, Y., and Kobatake, Y., *Bull. Tokyo Inst. Technol. Ser. B*, p. 199 (1958).
28. Snoddon, W. J., *Am. Soc. Testing Materials Spec. Tech. Publ. No.* **201**, 73 (1957).

CHAPTER 8

Experimental Strength of Adhints

§82. IN PROPER JOINTS, §15, with strong adherends rupture occurs in the adhesive. Let f_M be the tensile (or shear) strength of the adhesive material, determined on a usual bulk specimen (e.g., in the dogbone shape customary for tensile testing). Then, analogously to equation (67), we may write

$$\xi = (f_M + s_0)\beta_0, \tag{122}$$

ξ being again the molecular cohesion of the material, s_0 the residual stresses created during the preparation of the specimen, and β_0 the factor of stress concentration at the weakest spot in the sample. We assume that ξ in equation (122) is equal to ξ in equation (67). This means that we disregard the possibility of the adhesive in bulk being chemically different from the adhesive in the adhint; we do not admit, for instance, that the thin film present in the latter system may suffer a greater degree of oxidation in air than a more voluminous dogbone. Whenever anything of this kind takes place, no correlation between f_m of an adhesive joint and f_M of the bulk adhesive can be expected.

The values of s_0 and β_0, as a rule, will be different from the analogous magnitudes s and β for the adhint. The value of α is unity for one-component systems, §60. By combining (67) and (122) we obtain

$$\frac{f_m}{f_M} = \frac{\beta_0}{\alpha\beta} \frac{\xi - \beta s}{\xi - \beta_0 s_0}. \tag{123}$$

Thus, only rarely will f_m be equal to f_M, and the two quantities are likely to be similar only when α is not much greater than unity and β and s are not greatly different from β_0 and s_0.

Unfortunately, equation (123) is new and has not been tested yet. The enormous amount of information on the strength of adhints, which can be gathered from literature, cannot be used for this test chiefly because too often the investigator believed to have been measuring molecular adhesion, a primary quantity, and therefore paid no attention to the value of α, β, and s. A large proportion of data on adhesive joints has an extremely narrow range of validity, if any at all; we are told that joints having a definite range of f_m values have been prepared in a definite manner, but it is impossible to predict from this intelligence what will be the f_m of a joint prepared or tested in a slightly different way, see §99.

In an attempt to extract as much usefulness from published data as possible, these data are grouped so as to supply answers to the following problems:

1. Is there any correlation between the breaking stresses of adhints of different types (butt, lap, etc.)?

2. What is the effect of adhint dimensions?

3. How close is the correlation between the breaking stresses of adhints and adhesives?

4. How does the composition of an adhesive affect its strength in adhints?

5. What is the effect of the rate of loading and separation?

6. What is the effect of temperature?

7. What is the effect of environment?

Adhints of Different Types

§83.   CONSIDER ADHINTS depicted in Fig. 93. Left, a system ready for stripping is shown, see Fig. 87; the adhesive film, not marked, is between the ribbon and the plate. In Fig. 93, middle, the lower face of the ribbon is attached to a rigid plate, and plates A and B are pulled apart by a tensile force. Finally, in Fig. 93, right, the same plates are sheared as in a single lap joint. If the adhesive films in the three systems are identical, comparison of the forces needed for their rupture would show the effect of the straining procedure, that is whether by peeling, tensile pull, or shear. Since the residual stresses s and the microscopic stress concentration factors β, equation (123), are supposed to be identical, the contemplated comparison would give us infor-

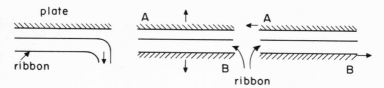

Fig. 93. Three different types of rupturing an adhint.

mation on the relative magnitude of factor α. If also the values of α were identical, the ratio of the peeling to the tensile force (for Hookean solids) would be $0.3799 \ (E/E_1)^{0.25}\delta^{0.75}h_0^{0.25}/l$ and the ratio of the tensile to the shear force, simply σ_m/τ_{max}; for the meaning of the symbols see equations (110), (111), and (100).

Apparently, of the three types sketched in Fig. 93, small values of $\alpha - 1$ are most readily achieved in butt joints. A butt joint, in which stress concentration depicted in Fig. 58 is believed to have been eliminated, is illustrated in Fig. 94 from reference 1. An amount of adhesive insufficient to fill the clearance between two cylinders is applied to their bases. When molten, it wets the two solids and forms an "hourglass-like" body. Because the

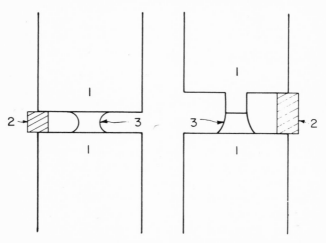

Fig. 94. Butt joints in which stress concentrations are relatively unimportant. From reference 1. 2: spacers; 3: adhesive.

waist of the hourglass has a smaller crosssection than the area
of the adherend–adhesive boundary, the adhesive breaks across
this waist; consequently, stress concentrations along the 3-phase
boundary line are of no importance. Evidently, the stress concentration indicated in Fig. 57 must exist in adhints of Fig. 94
but the central part of the hourglass seemingly was more like a
cylindrical column so that the magnitude of $\alpha - 1$ was moderate.
The rupture stress f_m in this arrangement should be computed
from $f_m = F_m/A_{min}$, A_{min} being the smallest cross section (i.e.,
through the waist) of the adhesive column; F_m is again the external force just causing fracture.

The value of $\alpha - 1$ seems to be small in many butt joints
produced in the customary manner because the adhesive–air
interface has a shape different from that postulated in §67. Since
liquid adhesives, as a rule, wet the adherends, §23, a film of the
adhesive remains, after setting, on the surfaces perpendicular to
the adherend-adhesive interface, see Fig. 94 right and 95. Stress
distribution in systems of this kind is unknown but it is highly
probable that factor α is smaller in these adhints than in those
of Figs. 57 and 58.

It is frequently observed that adhesives having a high modulus
(E_1) of elasticity and a small total relative elongation appear

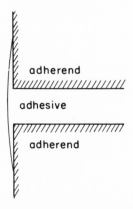

FIG. 95. A butt joint in which stress concentrations presumably are unimportant.

stronger in tensile (butt) than in stripping tests. This observation presumably can be accounted for in the following manner. When E_1 is large, it is less different from the modulus (E) of the adherend. Consequently, the magnitude of λ in equation (75), §67.2, is small and, thus, the stress concentration illustrated in Fig. 58 also is small. On the other hand, when an adhesive, whose maximum strain is small, is in contact with a flexible adherend (as employed in peeling tests), stress concentrations at the bend of the ribbon, see §80, must arise. Thus, $\alpha - 1$ is moderate in butt joints and excessive in peeling experiments.

§84.   THE BETTER UTILIZATION of the strength of an adhesive material in a butt joint as compared with a peel test can be recognized in measurements on polyethylene joints.[1, 2] As Fig. 102, §85, demonstrates, the breaking stress f_m of butt joints, in which $\alpha - 1$ was lessened by the artifice of Fig. 94 or a similar device, was consistently higher than f_M, §82, of the cement in bulk. The reasons for f_m being greater than f_M are discussed in §86 but they would not be sufficient if the α of the butt joints were great. On the contrary, Table IX, §79, shows that peeling force was one-third to one-sixth of that calculated without regard to stress concentrations. If s and β were identical in these two types of adhint, then α in the peel tests was 3 to 6 times as great as in the tensile tests. Unfortunately, we cannot be sure that the values of s and β really were indistinguishable in the two systems.

A comparison of butt, lap, and torque joints was performed[3] on adhints consisting of aluminum alloy adherends (the alloy contained copper and magnesium, had designation F44 and a very high value of Young's modulus) and "Metallon 130" (apparently, a cured epoxy resin) as the adhesive. Figure 96 presents f_m of butt joints (in kg. wt./mm.²; multiply by 98.1 to express it in bars) as function of the diameter (in cm.) of the buttons glued together. It is seen that the average breaking stress for the most favorable button diameter ($=3$ cm.) was about 6.3 kg. wt./mm.² (or 620 bars). The tensile strength of the adhesive in bulk covered the range between 490 and 760 bars, that is was almost identical with the f_m of the better joints. Lap joints between 0.1 cm. thick strips of the same alloy, with an

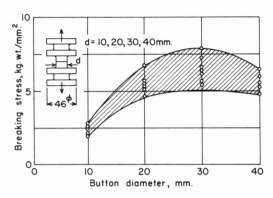

FIG. 96. Rupture stress in butt joints. Abscissa: diameter of the adherend buttons in cm. Ordinate: breaking stress in kg. wt./mm.[2] From reference 3.

overlap of 1 cm., gave f_m values near 250 bars. The difference between butt and lap joints could have been due to ratio σ_m/τ_{max} being about 2 to 3, see §83, but the results of the torque tests refute this hypothesis.

For torque tests, two short lengths of a tube (of the above aluminum alloy) were glued as illustrated in Fig. 97 and then one of them was rotated around the common axis. The details of calculating f_m from the force F_m needed to twist the adhint to rupture are not given; it is clear that the stress near the external boundary of adhesive and air was greater than that near the internal boundary; see §76. Figure 98 exhibits the f_m values (again in kg. wt./mm.[2]) as a function of the thickness h_0 (in mm.) of the adhesive film. The upper shaded region is for torque, and the lower, for lap tests. In twisting also τ_{max}, theoretically, is measured. Thus the values of 470 to 660 bars calculated for τ_{max} from the upper range of Fig. 98 are not in accord with the much lower values computed from the lower range; thus, the stress concentration factor α must have been larger in the lap joints.

Results of strength measurements on single lap, double lap and scarf joints can be found in §§72, 74, and 96.

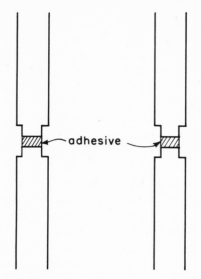

FIG. 97. A specimen for torque test.

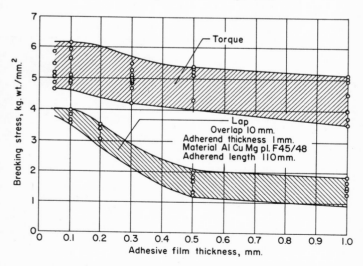

FIG. 98. Rupture stress and adhesive film thickness. Abscissa: film thickness in mm. Ordinate: breaking stress in kg. wt./mm.² Upper region for torque; lower region for lap tests. From reference 3.

Strength and Dimensions of an Adhint

§85.   THE CEMENT in every adhint has a thickness or a range of thicknesses; it has also a radius, or a width and a length, and so on. Also the adherends have linear dimensions. What is known about the correlation between the dimensions of the adhesive film and the adherends on one hand and the final strength of adhints on the other hand, is reviewed in this and the four following sections. The thickness h_0 of the cement film is discussed first.

The rule that "a joint is stronger the thinner the adhesive layer in it" has been established long ago by nonsystematic observations and mentioned many times in trade literature. Apparently the first scientific publication in which this rule was tested was a paper by Crow.[4] Copper cylinders, 0.63 cm. in diameter, were soldered (basis to basis) with the tin-lead eutectic alloy and broken in tension. Figure 99 shows the results. Its ordinate represents the breaking stress at which each joint failed, and the abscissa is the thickness of the solder film. In spite of the

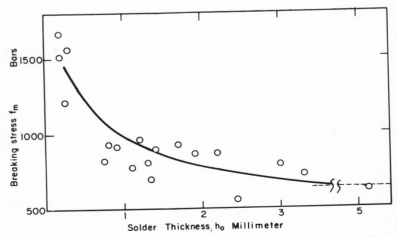

FIG. 99. Rupture stress and adhesive film thickness in soldered joints. Abscissa: film thickness in mm. Ordinate: breaking stress in bars. Data of reference 4.

poor precision of the experimental values, common to all measurements of the final strength of adhints, the tendency of f_m to increase when h_0 decreases is unmistakable. The discontinuous line at the right indicates the tensile strength of the solder (633 bars).

Similar tendency has been observed many times since. Thus, the strength of a commercial shellac adhesive between two nickel adherends[5] was 213–254 bars when the cement film was "extremely thin," 138–143 bars when h_0 was 0.30 mm., and 69–76 bars at $h_0 = 1.2$ mm. When two quartz cylinders were joined (basis to basis) with paraffin wax whose tensile strength was 7.31 bars, the f_m was 14.6, 14.5, 7.6, and 3.3 bars at h_0 equal to 0.003, 0.04, 0.07, and 2.5 mm., respectively.[6] One hundred parafin wax joints between a brass cylinder and a steel plate were broken in tension;[7] the maximum value of f_m was 34.3, the minimum was 14.2, and the arithmetic mean 24.1 bars when the thickness h_0 was approximately 0.057 mm., while the mean f_m of 40 joints having $h_0 = 0.54$ mm. was 14.6 bars.

Some of the more recent results, still for butt joints, are reproduced in Figs. 100, 101, and 102. Figure 100 is drawn according to the tables given in the original thesis.[8] Brass cylinders were soldered together by means of the tin-lead eutectic alloy Only the sound joints containing no visible bubbles were considered in constructing the figure. The values of f_m for narrow cylinders (diameter 1.17 ± 0.02 cm.) were combined by the present author into seven groups, of which only one represented a single measurement while the others contained three to five individual values. The average breaking stress and the average thickness for each group are shown by circles in the figure. An analogous procedure was applied to thicker cylinders (diameter 2.445 ± 0.045 cm.), except that only four groups were possible; the averages for these groups are represented by crosses. When Fig. 100 is compared with Fig. 99, it is clear that the reproducibility of rupture stress measurements did not markedly change from 1924 to 1949; and the properties of the eutectic solder, naturally, did not change either.

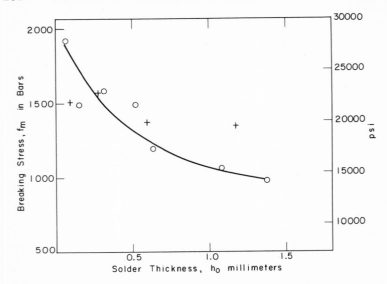

Fig. 100. Rupture stress and adhesive film thickness in soldered joints. Abscissa: film thickness in mm. Ordinate: breaking stress in bars. Circles: narrow cylinders. Crosses: thick cylinders. Data of reference 8.

Figure 101 is for poly(vinyl acetate) joints between two steel cylinders.[9] Breaking stress (the ordinate) is expressed in psi; multiply by 0.06895 to obtain f_m in bars. The thickness h_0 (the abscissa) is given in 0.001 inch; multiply by 25.4 to obtain h_0 in microns. The lines are, from top to bottom, for test temperatures of $-3°$, $22°$, $39°$, and $51°$C, respectively. The average molecular weight of the polymer was 225,000.

Figure 102 combines data[1] for a low-molecular polyethylene (molecular weight between 2500 and 3000, lower curve) and a high-molecular polyethylene (high-pressure, low-density type, upper curve). The adherends were: steel-to-glass for vertical lines, glass-to-glass for squares and crosses, and steel-to-steel for circles. All adhints were designed to minimize stress concentrations at the adherend-adhesive boundary. The discontinuous lines near the right-hand edge of the sketch indicate the tensile strength of the two polyethylenes, namely about 88 bars for the high and 56 bars for the low-molecular material.

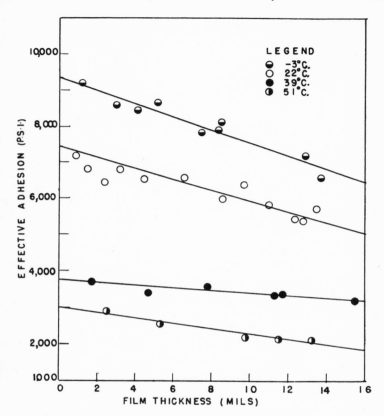

FIG. 101. Rupture stress and adhesive film thickness in poly(vinyl acetate) joints. Abscissa: film thickness in thousands of an inch. Ordinate: breaking stress in psi for test temperatures of $-3°$, $22°$, $39°$, and $51°$C.

§86. ALTHOUGH GRAPHS in Fig. 99 to 102 (and several analogous graphs in the literature) make decrease of f_m with increasing h_0 in butt joints certain, almost nothing can be said about the shape of the function $f_m = f(h_0)$. In several instances, the values of f_m at the lowest h_0 were smaller than at slightly higher h_0 values so that f_m seemed to have a maximum; see, for instance, the crosses in Fig. 102 and reference 10. However, it is generally believed that this decrease of f_m at extremely small

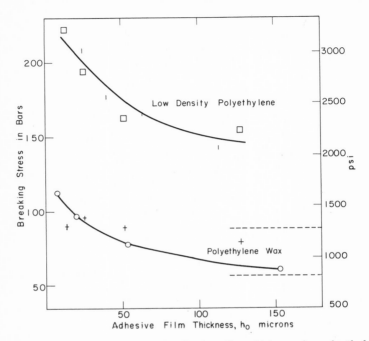

Fig. 102. Rupture stress and adhesive film thickness in polyethylene joints. Abscissa: film thickness in microns. Ordinate: breaking stress in bars. Discontinuous lines indicate the tensile strength of the polyethylenes. From reference 1.

cement thicknesses is due to the trivial circumstance that these adhesive films are likely to contain voids; when, in an attempt to produce a particularly thin joint, the experimenter applies a very small amount of the cement, this amount may be insufficient to fill the clearance between the two adherends; thus a *starved joint* may result.

If starved joints are disregarded, f_m monotonously decreases when h_0 increases. The curves of f_m versus h_0 are similar in Fig. 99, 100, and 102, but in Fig. 101 f_m appears to be a linear function of h_0; see also reference 11. Unfortunately, the cause of this discrepancy is not known. The results are too sketchy to decide whether and how the shape of the f_m-versus-h_0 curve depends on the adhesive, the adherends, the geometry of the joint, and so on. If we knew this shape for various adhints, the theory of the relation between thinness and strength were more explicit than it is now.

The values of h_0 can affect the value of f_m by altering either coefficient α, or β, or stress s, or two or three of these factors together. Consider the theoretical relation between β and h_0 first.

It is pointed out in §61 that the weakest spot in a sample is weaker the larger the sample. Thus, adhints with a thicker cement film are more likely to contain a particularly bad flaw than adhints in which there is less adhesive material. This theory has been tested by the method outlined in the last paragraph of §61. Ten groups of adhints, each of 10 samples 57 microns thick, were broken and the lowest breaking stresses for each group recorded.[7] In between, 40 samples of 540 microns each were measured. The average for the lowest rupture stresses of the thin joints (in groups of ten) would be approximately equal to the average of all rupture stresses of the thick joints, if the probability of flaws were the only factor influencing the relationship between f_m and h_0. As mentioned in §85, the latter average was 14.6 bars, and the former was 17.8 bars; and statistical analysis of the data proved that the difference between 17.8 and 14.6 was too great to be attributable to chance; thus, another factor (or factors) must also have contributed to the decrease of f_m with increasing h_0.

Factor β of equations (67) and (123) can be influenced by the thickness of the adhesive film also in virtue of another mechanism. The texture (e.g., the crystal size) of a solid depends on its rate of solidification. A thin film of molten adhesive between two metal adherends, as a rule, will solidify on cooling in a shorter time than a thick film of an identical material. Thus, the texture of the cement often will be different in a thin and in a thick joint; consequently, the strength of the adhesive also may be different in the two instances. This is true also when the adhesive sets because of the loss of solvent or because of a chemical reaction, see §40. For instance, polymerization of low-molecular unsaturated compounds usually is associated with evolution of heat; removal of heat is relatively more rapid when the volume in which reaction proceeds is smaller; thus, a thin film of polymer may form at a lower internal temperature than a thick one; and if the strength of the polymer depends on the formation temperature, the strength of this polymer in adhints will depend on h_0. This explanation was advanced for the above-mentioned difference between 17.8 and 14.6 bars,[7] but no experimental proof of the hypothesis exists.

Differences in the rate of setting between thin and thick adhints will, generally, cause differences in the intensity of the residual stresses s. These stresses may facilitate rupture, §43, but may also oppose it (as in hardened glass) and it is difficult to predict their effect on the function $f_m = f(h_0)$. Apparently, no experimental data of value for this discussion are available.

The effect of h_0 on the stress concentration factor α can approximately be deduced from the theories of §67. In particular equation (90) predicts that f_m should be inversely proportional to h_0 for rigid-plastic adhesives. None of the curves of Fig. 99 to 102 agrees with this prediction; for instance, for a substance as ductile as tin-lead eutectic alloy, the product $f_m h_0$, instead of being independent of h_0, increases from about 20–30 at the smallest h_0 to over 300 bars $\times$ cm. at the greatest thicknesses tested. Evidently, the assumptions on which equation (90) rests are not in accord with the experimental conditions employed.

Equation (90) includes another dimension of the adhint in addition to the thickness h_0. If the equation is applicable, f_m should be proportional to a/h_0 (i.e., radius/thickness). Unfortunately, the variation of f_m with h_0 is so small and the unavoidable scatter of the values of f_m so large that it is unsafe to decide whether f_m depends on a/h_0 or on h_0 alone. Preference for $f_m = f(a/h_0)$ was expressed, for instance, in references 8 and 12. In Fig. 100, crosses refer to adhints whose a was 2.1 times that of the adhints represented by circles. Consequently, to make f_m a function of h_0/a, the abscissa of the crosses should be reduced in the ratio 1 : 2.1. This translation would place the cross at the extreme right of the figure almost exactly on the curve for the thin joints, but the position of the other three crosses would not be improved. If f_m is plotted versus h_0/a, a rectangular hyperbola should result, but the experimental data for silver as the cement between two steel cylinders[12] afforded linear dependence between f_m and h_0/a. New experiments would be welcome.

Whatever the exact shape of the function $f_m = f(h_0)$, f_m seems to increase indefinitely when h_0 gets smaller and if starved joints are avoided; thus the strength of a butt joint should reach the strength of the adherend if the cement film is extremely thin. This state was almost achieved when two steel bars were joined by means of pure silver[11, 12] or some other metals.[11]

§87.   IN *lap joints*, rupture stress should often be approximately proportional to $\sqrt{h_0}$, see equations (100) and (103). The predicted increase of f_m with h_0 is visible in Fig. 86. If the two joints for which Fig. 86a and 86b are drawn were identical in all respects except the adhesive thickness h_0, then h_0 in Fig. 86b is 25 times as great as in Fig. 86a. The ordinates of these figures are proportional to breaking stress. It is seen that, for instance at the ratio of overlap to cement thickness equal to 10, the ordinate for the G-R curve in Fig. 86b is about four times as great as in Fig. 86a; thus f_m in this example increased fourfold when h_0 increased 25 times.

Those few publications, in which the experimental dependence of f_m on h_0 in single lap joints is treated, do not confirm the prediction of the theory. Breaking force F_m and breaking stress f_m seem to decrease when adhesive thickness h_0 increases, and with a gradient similar to that obtaining in butt joints, §86.

Thus, for aluminum and a Neoprene–phenolic adhesive the rupture stress was 3000 psi (≈ 207 bars) at h_0 of about 50 microns and 1200 psi (≈ 83 bars) at $h_0 = 508$ microns, and the decrease was similar for a "Buna N-phenolic resin."[10] It is true that a filled epoxy resin adhesive (consisting of 45 parts resin and 55 parts alumina + asbestos) showed breaking stresses independent of h_0 when this varied from 250 to about 750 microns, for both butt and single lap joints,[13] but the range of thicknesses perhaps was too narrow to detect the effect of h_0.

Decrease of f_m on increasing h_0 in single lap joints can be seen in Fig. 98, §84. The ribbons (1 mm. thick, 20 mm. wide) were of an Al-Cu-Mg alloy, a commercial epoxy resin ("Araldite I") was the adhesive, and the overlap was 10 mm. long. The lower band refers to lap joints.

A similar behavior is exhibited in Fig. 103 whose ordinate is

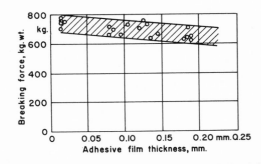

FIG. 103. Rupture stress and adhesive film thickness in lap joints. Abscissa: film thickness in mm. Ordinate: breaking force in kg. wt. From reference 14.

force F_m (in kg. wt.) required to break single lap joints of thickness h_0 (in mm.) plotted along the abscissa.[14] The adherends were 1 mm. thick and 25 mm. wide ribbons of an Al-Cu-Mg alloy, and the adhesive was an epoxy resin apparently similar to, or identical with, that used in the tests of Fig. 98. The absolute values of F_m are in good agreement with the f_m values of Fig. 98 as these have to be multiplied by 200 mm.^{2} (i.e., 20 mm. × 10 mm.) to obtain F_m.

It is not known whether the discrepancy between these experimental results and the theory is caused by (a) the inexactitude of the calculation of the stress concentration factor α, equation (67), §60 or (b) by the influence of factor β which almost always tends to be greater in thicker cement films, or (c) the difference in the magnitude of s stresses in thin and thick joints.

A very peculiar observation has been made[14] on the dependence of the "fatigue" of a lap joint on its thickness. Single lap joints, similar to those whose behavior is summarized in Fig. 103 and thus having resistances to fracture of 600 to 800 kg. wt., were loaded with 100 kg. each and left in air at 20° and 35–45% relative humidity. The adhint in which the adhesive was about 20 microns thick broke after about 20 hours, the adhints whose h_0 was between 40 and 120 microns lasted 300 to 500 hours, and those having h_0 near 180 microns yielded after less than an hour. No explanation is available for the short endurance times of very thin and relatively thick adhesive films.

The effect of the adherend thickness δ on the breaking force was mentioned in §72. Another example[15] deals with plates of an Al-Mg-Mn alloy glued with a phenol-vinyl-formaldehyde adhesive. When, at a constant overlap of 10 mm., δ increased from 0.5 to 2 mm., the force increased in the ratio 1.4 : 1.

§88. FORCE NEEDED to *peel* a joint would be proportional to $h_0^{0.25}$, see equation (110), if all the ingredients of the adhint were Hookean solids, if stress concentrations reported in §79 were absent, and if the angle of peel is 90°.

Experiments, which are in a semiquantitative agreement with this expectation, have been made with a Thiokol adhesive between cotton duck and rigid aluminum plates.[10] The angle of peel, however, was 180°. Peeling force per cm. width was about 8×10^5 dynes at $h_0 = 40$ microns, about 34×10^5 dynes at $h_0 = 750$ microns, and 53×10^5 dynes at $h_0 = 1600$ microns (i.e., 1.6 mm.). Unfortunately, determination of the thickness of an adhesive film on a crudely porous material, such as cotton duck, is not always convincing. This remark applies also to some experiments on rubber adhesives.[16]

In another set of experiments[14] stripping force decreased when the cement thickness increased, i.e., the behavior was similar to that of butt joints, §85. The adherends were made of a weak Al-Mg-Si alloy whose yield stress at 0.2% strain was approximately 600 bars; the ribbons were 0.8 mm. thick and 25 mm. wide. An epoxy cement, same as used for the experiments of Fig. 103, was the adhesive. The peeling angle apparently was not kept constant. When h_0 increased from about 0.02 to 0.19 mm., peeling tension (kilodynes per cm.) decreased from about

8000 to about 6800. Peeling force, at a peel angle of 180°, was independent of thickness[17] in the range between 152 and 557 microns but its absolute value was so small (about 100 kilodynes/cm.) that the presence of a weak boundary layer, §15, may be suspected; the system consisted of chrome-tanned gelatin, a butadiene–acrylonitrile polymer (as the adhesive) and a percale fabric. Obviously, new experiments designed with due regard to the present knowledge of peel mechanism are needed.

In the *twist* experiments whose results are summarized in Fig. 98, §84, the dependence of f_m on h_0 evidently was quite small; no explanation for this observation seems to exist.

§89.   THE EFFECT of the diameter of the adhesive film on the final strength of a butt joint was mentioned in §86.

The importance of the width of a lap joint apparently has not been systematically studied. Because many lap joints fail in peel and because breaking tension (i.e., force per unit width) needed for stripping some adhesives depends on this width, §79, some dependence of f_m on width in lap joints may be expected.

For the dependence of f_m on the length of the cement film (i.e., on the length of overlap) see §72.

The length of the adhesive film which is still attached to the plate in stripping tests must influence the peeling strength, if this length is very short, but no effect was noticed when it was, say, 200 times the combined thickness of ribbon and adhesive, or greater.

Those dimensions of the adherends, which are independent of the dimensions of the cement film, have been but little investigated in their relation to the mechanical strength of adhints. In butt joints, the extension of the adherends in the direction normal to the adherend–adhesive interface (such as the length of the cylinders in Fig. 58) should be irrelevant as long as the cylinders are long enough. In lap joints, the effect of thickness δ of the adherends is exemplified in Fig. 70, §72. Its abscissa represents $(L/\delta)^2$; if the overlap is constant, it is proportional to δ^{-2}. When L/δ is small, that is δ is great, $F_m/w\delta$ is an almost linear function of log δ, i.e.,

$$\frac{F_m}{w\delta} = k_1 - k_2 \log \delta \text{ or } F_m = (k_1 - k_2 \log \delta)w\delta, \quad (124)$$

k_1 and k_2 being constants. Thus, F_m increases with δ but less than linearly. This behavior was noticed several times. For instance,[18] the F_m of a lap joint between two magnesium panels increased in the ratio 2 : 1 when the thickness of the panels increased from 0.25 cm. to 1.4 cm.; and an equal increase in the δ of aluminum panels raised F_m in the ratio 2.2 : 1.

In peeling, the thickness δ of the ribbon should influence F_m/w according to equation (110). In some experiments[2] the effect was smaller than predicted. When aluminum ribbons were attached to rigid glass with a polyethylene and then stripped off, the ratio of F_m (or F_m/w) values for a ribbon of 0.0076 cm. to that of a ribbon having $\delta = 0.0025$ cm. was about 1.8 for a brittle and about 0.9 for a ductile adhesive. The theoretical ratio is 2.3. As the dangerous stress concentrations occur in different regions of the adhint when the brittleness of the cement varies, §§79 and 80, a difference between the above ratios for brittle and ductile materials would be expected but no account is possible yet for the experimental numerical values.

Strength of Adhints and of Adhesives

§90.   THE RATIO of the strength (f_m) of adhints to that (f_M) of adhesives in bulk is given by equation (123), §82. As the quantities appearing in this equation have never been all determined for an adhint and its adhesive in bulk, only semiquantitative or frankly qualitative correlations between f_m and f_M can be hoped for from experimental data.

A clear correlation is demonstrated in Fig. 102. If the curves of f_m versus h_0 are extrapolated to great values of h_0, the values of f_m will approach those of f_M marked as dicontinuous lines.

The graph combines data for two polyethylene samples. A third type also was used; it had (allegedly) a molecular weight near 100,000 and was of a high-density kind. Also for this material, extrapolation of the $f_m - h_0$ curve leads to values almost identical with the experimental tensile strength of the bulk polyethylene[1].

In the adhints of Fig. 102, $\alpha - 1$ apparently was very small, see §83. Since the bulk specimens of the polyethylenes were prepared in conditions similar to those used for the preparation of the adhints, the shrinkage stresses s and s_0 presumably had similar magnitudes. Thus the difference between f_m and f_M probably was caused chiefly by the difference between β and β_0; as these two quantities are likely to be nearly identical when h_0 is large, an accord between f_M on one hand and f_m extrapolated to $h_0 = \infty$ on the other hand may be expected.

Similarity between f_m and f_M exists also when no attempt is made to reduce α to unity. Two examples, for the eutectic solder and for paraffin wax, are mentioned in §85, and a third, for "Metallon 130," in §84. The tensile strength of ice a few degrees below the melting point usually lies between 10 and 18 bars; and the strength of adhints in which copper, steel, or glass were joined together with ice proved to be near 19 bars.[19] The strength of soldered joints is similar to the bulk strength of the solder whatever the ratio of tin to lead in the latter.[20]

§91.   As LONG AS the magnitudes of f_m and f_M are similar, all adhints made with a definite cement should have comparable breaking stresses independent of the nature of the adherend. This obviously is true for many commercial adhesives because their manufacturers claim (in technical leaflets, not only in advertisements) relatively narrow ranges of strength, e.g., between 2000 and 2500 psi, for their products without specifying the adherends, the geometry of the joints, and so on. Some examples of f_m being almost independent of the adherends in controlled experiments are mentioned in the earlier sections of this monograph, for instance in §§85 and 90. In general, of course,

f_m must depend on the mechanical properties of the adherends since these affect the stress distribution in the cement film.

As long as f_m and f_M are similar, the strength of adhints made with various adhesives should fall in an order independent of the adherends. Thus, §90, joints made with the strongest polyethylene were stronger than those made with the second best, which in their turn were stronger than those made with the weakest polymer, whatever the adherends (stainless steel or glass). A more extensive comparison is reproduced in Table X from reference 21.

A is a poly(vinyl acetate), B a cellulose nitrate, C a resorcinol–formaldehyde resin, D casein, E gum arabic, F smoked sheet rubber, and G Neoprene. The order of strengths is not identical for all adherends but the discrepancies apparently can be accounted for by special circumstances. For instance, casein glue and gum arabic set because of loss of water; this loss is more rapid with porous adherends such as paper-phenolic laminate and birch wood; hence, these two solids gave rise to higher strengths with D and E than some nonporous adherends; in other words, in these systems the order of adhesives was not constant because the adhesive substances were different in contact with different adherends. Also, some adherends were weakened by some adhesives (e.g., paper-phenolic laminate by casein glue). Finally, weak boundary layers evidently were not always avoided; thus adhesive C gave zero strengths with glass and metals both in butt and in double lap joints.

TABLE X

ORDER OF STRENGTH OF BUTT JOINTS WITH DIFFERENT
ADHERENDS AND ADHESIVES

Adherend	Adhesives
Stainless steel	$A > B > D > F > G > E > C$
Aluminum alloy	$A > B > F > G > D > E > C$
Paper-phenolic laminate	$A > B > C > D > E > G > F$
Glass	$A > B > E > G > F > C > D$
Birch wood	$C > B > D > A > E > G > F$
Hard rubber	$C > B > A > E > G > D > F$

Strength of Adhints and Composition of Adhesives

§92.   WHEN A NEW ADHESIVE is being formulated in industry, the composition is varied until the desired (or a compromise) strength is attained. Thus, relation between the composition of a cement and the strength of adhints made with this cement has been and is being studied in numerous laboratories on numberless systems. Some of the results thus obtained are deposited in patents, and a small percentage finds its way into scientific and technical literature. Unfortunately, even this selected minority of abundant research reports too often has no value for the science of adhesive joints. This is so because the materials used for the formulation in too many instances are poorly characterized and, perhaps, do not exist anymore since their manufacture was discontinued; and because the tests were conducted without any theory or with the guidance by a wrong theory, which means that the experimenter did not know what parameters should be controlled to obtain results of general validity.

A logical way of studying the relation between composition and strength would be

a. in proper joints, §15,—investigate the relation between the composition of a material and its tensile or shear strength (f_M); compare this f_M with the strength f_m of adhints; find out what combination of the parameters α, β, and s, equation (123), caused the difference between f_M and f_m; and

b. in improper joints—investigate the relation between the composition of an adhesive and its ability to form weak boundary layers at the interfaces with different adherends.

A procedure similar to that advocated under a. was described in §90; when α was made almost equal to unity, β was almost equal to β_0, and s almost equal to s_0, f_m was approximately equal to f_M. For an example of procedure b. see §49 on the correlation between the sulfur content of a rubber mix and its reactivity with brass.

§93.   ONLY A FEW of the attempts to establish empirical relations between glue composition and adhint strength, without any regard to either f_M or weak boundary layers, can be outlined here.

In butt joints, rupture stress of poly(vinyl acetate) fractions between steel cylinders increased[9] with the molecular weight (M.W.) of the fraction as long as this was 150,000 or less, but there was no significant difference between the strengths of adhints made with polymers of M.W. = 147,000 and M.W. = 225,000; at the thickness of the cement film equal to 25 microns, breaking stress was about 228, 393, and 490 bars (3300, 5700, and 7100 psi) for the average molecular weights of 54,000, 77,000, and above 140,000.[22] This presumably was the effect of the tensile strength of the adhesive since this also in many instances increases with M.W. to a limiting value.

Other examples of butt joints are more complicated. The basis faces of two aluminum cylinders[22] were coated with a 10% solution of a copolymer of polystyrene $(100 - x$ parts) with acrylic acid (x parts) in a solvent, dried at 80°C so that coatings approximately 50 microns thick remained on each face, pressed together, and heated for 15 to 20 min. at 180°C. Then the breaking stress f_m of the adhints was measured. When benzene was the solvent, f_m was about 80 bars for polystyrene alone, 320 bars at $x = 1$, and 210 bars at $x = 3$. Thus, the conclusion could be reached that in the copolymer series studied the maximum of "adhesiveness" is achieved near $x = 1$. But the results were strikingly different when 2.4-pentadione was used as the solvent. In this instance, f_m remained between 290 and 320 bars at all values of x between 2 and 24. Methyl ethyl ketone, pyridine, and ethyl acetate, as solvents, took up intermediate positions between 2.4-pentadione and benzene. The reason for this solvent effect is not known but it may have been trivial. Suppose that, as often happens, tensile strength of the copolymer increases with x; then, for proper joints, f_m also is likely to increase with x. This, of course, presupposes a healthy joint. If the consistency of the copolymer at 180°C also increases with x (a very reasonable assumption), the constant duration of heating may be sufficient to eliminate air bubbles at low values of x but insufficient at $x > 1$; this would account for the maximum of f_m at

$x = 1$ in the instance of benzene solutions. When a higher boiling solvent (or one which more slowly evaporates from the copolymer) is employed, the adhesive film after drying at 80° may still contain enough solvent to act as a plasticizer; thus the consistency of the cement at 180° is lower and elimination of gas bubbles is achieved also at $x > 1$. As long as this or a similar possibility is not shown to be absent, the meaning of the experiments is doubtful.

Another example [23] concerns lap joints between clad aluminum strips, the adhesives being a series of epoxy resins cured with phthalic anhydride. The exact structure of the cured adhesive naturally was not known, but the series contained, for one epoxy group, 0.85 molecule of anhydride and $n[-0 \cdot C_6H_4 \cdot C(CH_3)_2 \cdot C_6H_4 \cdot O \cdot CH_2 \cdot CHOH \cdot CH_2 -]$ groups, and n covered the range between 0.05 and 5. Rupture stress of the adhints was 151 to 159 bars (2191 to 2313 psi) as long as n was greater than, say, 1.5, but at $n < 0.5$ it was 118 to 124 bars (1708 to 1794 psi). As shear strength of cured epoxy resins usually increases with n, the above observation can simply be accounted for as another example of the common parallelism between f_m and f_M, see §90. If we wish to emphasize the effect of composition, we may state that f_m increases with the molecular weight of the resin, or with the number of hydroxyl groups in it, or with the number of isopropylidene groups $(:C(CH_3)_2)$, or decreases on an increase in the number of benzene rings; many such correlations are possible. Hence, the correlation between f_m and the volume density of OH groups, preferred by the experimenter, does not appear convincing.

§94.   THREE EXAMPLES may be mentioned for peeling.

Two polymers, one containing 85% vinyl chloride and 15% vinyl acetate, and the other consisting of 85% vinyl chloride, 9.3% vinyl acetate, and 5.7% maleic acid, were mixed in various proportions, plasticized with a nonspecified mixture of plasticizers and used to coat sheets of regenerated cellulose containing 16% glycerol; then two coated strips were heat sealed together, kept at 35% relative humidity for 24 hours, and peeled apart.[24] As long as the ratio of the two polymers was greater than 96 : 4

(i.e., the concentration of maleic acid was less than 0.342%), peeling force increased with the percentage of maleic acid; e.g., at 10° peeling tension (=force/width) was approximately 18, 49, and 78 kilodynes/cm. when this percentage was 0.03%, 0.09%, and 0.34%, respectively. It was concluded that "adhesion" increased with the concentration of free acid according to a kind of Freundlich's adsorption isotherm. Regrettably, the acidity of the film was not measured. Maleic anhydride would react, for instance, with glycerol and form esters; in this case, vinyl acetate would be supplanted by maleic acid esters rather than by free acid, i.e., the comparison would be between two different esters. As none of the quantities needed to calculate peeling force, see §77, was ascertained, it is impossible to decide where the rupture occurred. However, the low values of the peeling tension would better agree with the existence of a weak boundary layer.

That chemical activity, contrary to the authors' view, was not important, can be concluded from some later measurements.[25] When, in copolymers, the mole fraction of methyl vinyl ketone was increased at the expense of either styrene or vinyl acetate, the improvement in peeling resistance was very similar; from the viewpoint of the chemical theory of adhesion, §59.2, substitution of a ketone for a hydrocarbon should greatly enhance the adhesion to cellulose but substitution of a ketone for an ester is more likely to lower this adhesion.

A system in which stripping force, again with Cellophane, was smaller the greater the percentage of "chemically active" groups was found in copolymers of butadiene and acrylonitrile.[26] The Cellophane was not plasticized. It was coated with a copolymer solution in which a percale fabric was embedded, see §88, and the fabric was stripped off after the evaporation of the solvent. The peeling tension (kilodynes per centimeter width) was about 1600, 1400, and 130 when the percentage of acrylonitrile was 18.4, 28.6, and 37.7%, respectively. The visible character of rupture also varied with the nitrile content. The first adhesive (i.e., that containing 18.4% $CH_2: CHCN$) broke clearly in cohesion, the second was severed partly in the middle and partly near a boundary of the cement film, and the third ruptured only near a boundary. The difference could have been accounted for by a shift of the dangerous stress concentration from the center to the boundary, as happened, for instance, when the brittleness of the adhesive increased, §§79 and 80. However, the value of 130 kilodynes/cm. seems to be too small to be explained by stress concentrations; presumably, a weak boundary layer was present. The presence of such a layer is even more probable in the system of Cellophane and a copolymer of butadiene 1 + styrene 1 which broke near the interface at the peeling tension of 14 kilodynes/cm., while another copolymer containing 2.3 parts butadiene for 1 part of styrene required over 1300 kilodynes/cm.

Finally, a study may be mentioned in which a weak boundary layer was deliberately although unwittingly produced.[27] Polymer films were cast on, and then peeled off, glass plates previously equilibrated with saturated water vapor; thus, a water-rich zone initially existed between the glass and the polymer. However, the polymer was applied as a solution (in an organic solvent) and solvent was removed by evaporation before the peeling test; thus it is not known how much, if any, water was still present on the glass surface during the stripping. The experimental values for peeling tension were, for instance, benzyl cellulose 72, cellulose nitrate 59, ethyl cellulose 24, and cellulose acetate 13 kilodynes/cm. The significance of this series, even assuming that it is reproducible, is obscure.

Rate of Loading and of Rupture

§95   THE EFFECT of rate of loading on the strength of adhints would be expected to be determined above all by the influence of this rate on the tensile or shear strength or plasticity of the adhesive (or, in improper joints, of the weak boundary layer). Apparently, no systematic comparison between the adhint strength f_m and the adhesive strength f_M at different rates of loading has ever been carried out. An analogous remark may be made concerning the length of time during which a given adhint or a given bulk specimen can support a definite load; or the rate of stripping (in an adhint or in a bulk adhesive) in its dependence on stripping force.

The effect of peeling tension on the rate of peeling is easy to determine. A few of the many published examples are reproduced here.

Figure 104 refers[28] to peeling of a 38-micron thick aluminum ribbon attached to a glass reinforced laminate with an epoxy resin cross-linked with diethylenetriamine. The ordinate shows peeling tension in gram-weight per inch (multiply with 0.386 to obtain it in kilodynes/cm.) on the logarithmic scale, and rate of stripping (in inches/min., multiply with 0.042 to express it in cm./sec.) is plotted, again logarithmically, along the abscissa. The curves show the slight effect of surface treatment (solvent cleaned and chemically cleaned) and also the effect of the angle

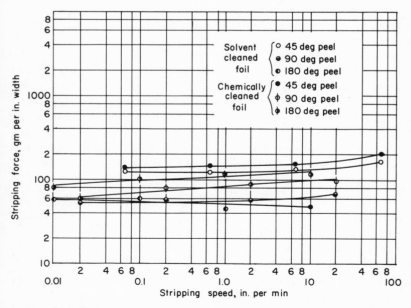

Fig. 104. Peeling force and peeling rate. Absscisa: log of rate of stripping in inch/min. Ordinate: log of peeling tension in g. wt./inch. From reference 28.

of peel, see §81. As far as the rate is concerned, it is clear that its influence was small; when rate u increased in the ratio 1000 : 1, peeling tension rose only in a ratio 1.2 : 1 or a similar ratio.

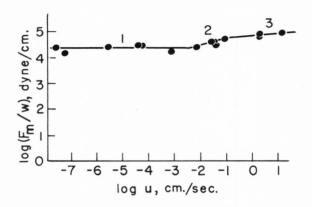

FIG. 105. Peeling force and peeling rate. Abscissa: log of rate of stripping ·in cm./sec. Ordinate: log of peeling tension in dynes/cm. From reference 27.

Another example of peeling tension being almost independent of rate u is shown in Fig. 105 which presumably refers to splitting a weak boundary layer,[27] see §94. The ordinate is log (F_m/w) (i.e., of peeling tension, in dyne/cm.) and the abscissa is log u (in cm./sec.). A cellulose acetate film was peeled off glass. Numbers 1, 2, and 3 indicate three sections of the curve which are said to correspond to different stripping mechanisms. It is seen that increase of u in the enormous ratio of 10^8 : 1 caused an increase of F_m/w in a ratio of about 5 : 1.

Results of clearly cohesive failures in the cement film are summarized[16] in Fig. 106. Two pieces of a fabric, 1.5 inch wide, were impregnated with a rubber cement, pressed together, and then pulled apart at a peel angle of 180°. Peeling force in lb. wt. (multiply with 117 to obtain peeling tension in kilodynes/cm.) is plotted along the abscissa, while the speed of stripping in inch/min. (multiply with 0.042 to have it in cm./sec.) is shown on the ordinate. Curves A, B, and C are for film thicknesses of 0.0063, 0.013, and 0.019 cm., respectively.

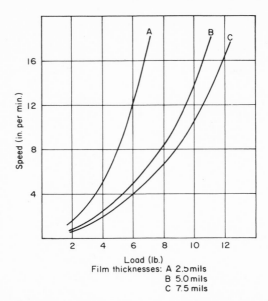

Film thicknesses: A 2.5 mils
B 5.0 mils
C 7.5 mils

Fɪɢ. 106. Peeling force and peeling rate. Ordinate: rate of stripping in inch/min. Abscissa: peeling force in lb. wt. for three different film thicknesses. From reference 16.

In several instances, rate of stripping affected not only peeling tension but also the type of rupture. Thus[16] some rubber-based adhesives broke clearly in the cement film when u was small (e.g., 0.1 cm./sec.) but parting occurred near the interface when u was great (e.g., 2 cm./sec.); and the magnitude of u at which the transition from clearly cohesive to apparently adhesive failure took place, was less the greater the degree of vulcanization of the rubber.

Also when adhints of "percale fabric—a copolymer of butadiene and acrylonitrile—chrome tanned gelatin"[17] were peeled apart, ruptures far from the interface occurred only at the smallest rate tested (0.083 cm./sec.) while at all higher rates (0.17 to 0.30 cm./sec.) separation at the interface was observed.

The dependence of the type of rupture on stripping rate might be caused by the maximum strain effect outlined in §80.

The curvature of the ribbon at the "knee" as a rule will be greater (i.e., the radius of curvature will be smaller) on increasing rate u. Thus the strain in the ribbon at the boundary with adhesive also will increase with u; as soon as this strain exceeds the total relative elongation of the adhesive, this will crack near the boundary thus simulating an interfacial failure.

When rate of loading cross-lap joints was doubled,[29] breaking stress of a rubbery cement was little affected but that of two brittle adhesives increased in ratios ranging from 1.06 to 1.14. For single lap joints of a vinyl-phenolic adhesive the time before failure increased, for instance, in the ratio 250 : 1 when stress in the adhesive decreased from 240 to 180 bars.[30] In butt joints of poly(vinyl acetate) between steel cylinders rupture stress went up about 15% when rate of separation increased eighty-fold.[9]

§96.   AN ADHINT can be broken by repeated application of a load too weak to cause instantaneous rupture. Only one example of this effect can be described here. Two strips, 1.5 mm. thick, of an Al-Cu-Mg alloy were used to make either single lap or scarf joints with, apparently, an epoxy adhesive. Then tension was applied to them about 2000 times a minute, the stress varying each time between zero and a maximum value f. The magnitude of f (in kg. wt./mm.^{2}, multiply with 98.1 to express it in bars) is shown on the ordinate of Fig. 107; its abscissa means the number of pulls before the cement or a metal strip broke down; the metal failures are marked with 4-ray stars, and circles with arrows mean that the test was stopped before any fracture took place. The upper range of values refers to scarf joints, and it is seen that they are much stronger than single lap joints (the lower range) for all stresses tested. The highest stress applied to scarf joints was about one-half the tensile strength of the adhesive.[3] For reports on analogous experiments see references 14 and 30.

Effect of Temperature

§97.   THE EFFECT of temperature on the strength of adhints should be different in proper and in improper joints. As long as separation takes place in the adhesive, the temperature coeffi-

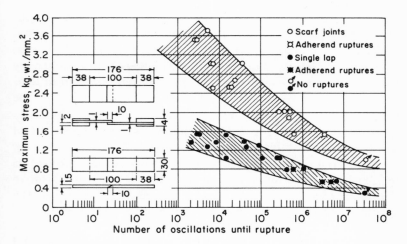

FIG. 107. Fatigue of an adhint. Abscissa: number of pulls before rupture. Ordinate: maximum value of pull in kg. wt./mm.² Upper range: scarf joints. Lower range: single lap joints. From reference 3.

cient of breaking stress f_m will be determined by the temperature coefficients of α, β, ξ, and s, see equation (67), §60. When a weak boundary layer is present, its changes with temperature will be decisive.

A few of the random observations reported in the literature are recorded here.

Butt and lap joints between copper adherends were made with a mixture of an epoxy-amine adhesive (9 parts) and alumina and asbestos filler (11 parts). The strength of the butt joints was about 500 bars between 20°K ($= -253$°C) and 300°K ($= 27$°C) but the lap joints broke at about 70 bars at 20°K and 70°K and at about 250 bars at 300°K.[13]

Single lap joints between 1-mm. thick strips of an Al-Cu-Mg alloy; a commercial adhesive apparently of the epoxy type. Strength was constant (220–260 bars) between -40° and 70°C but decreased to about 100 bars at 100° and 20 bars at 150°.[3]

Again single lap joints between aluminum alloy (7178-T6 clad) strips; ratio of overlap length to bar thickness 30, a vinyl-phenolic adhesive. Breaking stress was highest between 40° and 60°C; at −75° it was 0.5 to 0.9 of the maximum value, and at 200° it sank to about 0.1 of it.[30]

Single lap joints, aluminum alloy 24T-3 clad, a phenol-epoxy adhesive. Shear strength at 27° was about 120 bars and at 260° only about 40 bars, although at least one modification of the cement improved its heat resistance.[31]

There are conflicting data on the temperature coefficient of the strength of adhints in which ice is the adhesive.[19, 32, 33]

In at least one respect the effect of temperature is analogous to that of the rate of separation, see §95. Some adhints broke clearly in cohesion when temperature was high and near the interface when it was low. This was noticed, for instance, in peeling leather attached to another leather strip with a rubber cement;[34] in this system the "low" temperature was −20° and the "high," +50°C.

It is possible by special experiments to determine whether ξ or s determine the temperature dependence of adhint strength. An adhesive containing phenol-formaldehyde and vinyl butyral was employed in these tests.[35] When aluminum–aluminum and steel–steel joints were heated and then broken at room temperature, the loss in strength was less for the former than for the latter systems; this presumably was caused by the difference in thermal stresses because the difference between the coefficients of heat expansion of adhesive and aluminum was less than that between adhesive and steel. When the joints were strongly cooled for a while and then broken at room temperature, the decrease in their rupture stress was smaller than after a temperature increase of a comparable magnitude; apparently, the deleterious effect of temporary heating included also a chemical change resulting in a lower value of ξ, see §51, while cooling was not associated with a chemical reaction.

Effect of Environment

§98. IN GENERAL, environment can affect the strength of an adhint through the adherend, the adhesive, or a boundary layer. Thus, no joint between two pieces of sugar and no joint in which sucrose is the adhesive is likely to be water-resistant. A greater interest attaches to cases in which neither the adherend nor the cement are affected but the adhint is weakened because of formation of a weak boundary layer or because of another process more or less specific for adhesive joints. An example of this kind is reviewed in detail in §51.

When lap joints between plates of aluminum alloys, cured epoxy resin being the adhesive, were immersed in distilled water for about a year, the final strength was 10–25% of the initial if the alloy contained copper (and magnesium) but about 40% of the initial strength was retained if magnesium and silicon were the main alloying elements.[14] In some instances corrosion of the copper alloy was discernible under the adhesive film. The gradual formation of a weak boundary layer was noticeable also in that fresh adhints failed clearly in cohesion while aged specimens broke near an interface.

The effect of prestressing on endurance in water may be referred to here although it has been studied[36] on systems which cannot qualify as adhesive joints. When a fabric of glass fibers is embedded in a polymeric substance (a polyester or a cured epoxy resin) and then stretched, the stress-strain curve exhibits a "knee"; at stresses below the kink the modulus of elasticity is greater than at higher stresses. Apparently the system (called a laminate) behaves as one material in the first and as two materials in the second region, and the matrix ceases to follow the deformation of the fabric when stresses increase beyond the "knee." The cracks thus produced near the glass-polymer interface cause a kink also in the curve representing water uptake as a function of prestressing. When, for instance, the direction change in the stress-strain curve occurred between 0.5 and 0.6 f_M, f_M being the ultimate tensile strength of the laminate, then laminates prestressed to 0.4 f_M and then immersed in water (in unstressed state) for several weeks took up as little water as the specimens never subjected to a deliberate stress; but when the stress before immersion amounted to 0.7 f_M, water uptake was almost twice that of never stressed samples.

Unfortunately nothing is known on the mechanism of the advance of oxygen along the adherend-adhesive interface in the example of §51 or of the analogous advance of water in the examples of this section. Presumably diffusion of oxygen or water molecules is too slow to account for the rates observed. Probably, volume changes associated with the chemical reactions described above are essential for the rapidity of the process. Oxidation of the cement at the 3-phase line gives rise to grains of a new substance, and the pores between the grains permit oxygen rapidly to reach the deeper layers of the adhesive. Also the copper compounds formed in the aluminum alloy presumably contain intercrystalline spaces into which water is sucked because of capillarity. In the example of laminates, swelling of glass filaments in water may not only increase the wettability of the fibers and, consequently, the capillary pressure driving water into cracks, §22, but also cause additional cracks as a result of the volume increase of the filaments. When the adherends are electrical conductors, weakening of adhints in water or humid air may be due to electric currents between different points on the adherend surface, §9.

The numerous reported tests on the deterioration of adhints in distilled water, sea water, salt water spray, and so on, contain no answer to the problems outlined in the preceding paragraph.

REFERENCES

1. Bikerman, J. J., and Huang, C.-R., *Trans. Soc. Rheology* **3**, 5 (1959).
2. Bikerman, J. J., *J. Appl. Polymer Sci.* **2**, 216 (1959).
3. Winter, H., and Krause, G., *Aluminium* **33**, 669 (1957).
4. Crow, T. B., *J. Soc. Chem. Ind. (London)* **43**, 65 T (1924).
5. McBain, J. W., and Lee, W. B., *J. Phys. Chem.* **31**, 1674 (1927).
6. Konstantinova, W. P., *Acta physicochim. U.R.S.S.* **1**, 286 (1934).
7. Bikerman, J. J., *J. Soc. Chem. Ind. (London)* **60**, 23 (1941).
8. Baldauf, G. H., Thesis, M. I. T. 1949; Meissner, H. P., and Baldauf, G. H., *Trans. Am. Soc. Mech. Engrs.* **73**, 697 (1951).
9. Lasoski, S. W., and Kraus, G., *J. Polymer Sci.* **18**, 359 (1955).
10. Koehn, G. W., "Adhesion and Adhesives. Fundamentals and Practice," p. 120. Wiley, New York, 1954.
11. Bredzs, N., *Welding J.* **33**, 545 s (1954).

12. Moffatt, W. G., and Wulff, J., *J. Metals* **1957**, 442.

13. McClintock, R. M., and Hiza, M. J., *Modern Plastics* **35**, No. 10, 172 (1958).

14. Wellinger, K., and Rembold, U., *VDI Zeitschrift* **100**, 41 (1958).

15. Winter, H., *Z. Flugwiss.* **3**, 87 (1955).

16. Hammond, G. L., and Moakes, R. C. W., *Trans. Inst. Rubber Ind.* **25**, 172 (1949).

17. Shapovalova, A. I., Voyutskii, S. S., and Pisarenko, A. P., *Kolloid. Zhur.* **18**, 485 (1956).

18. Muchnik, S. N., *Mech. Eng.* **78**, 19 (1956).

19. Kobeko, P. P., and Marei, F. I., *Zhur. Tekh. Fiz.* **16**, 277 (1946).

20. Nightingale, S. J., "Tin Solders." Brit. Non-Ferrous Metals Res. Assoc. London, 1932.

21. DeLollis, N. J., Rucker, N., and Wier, J. E., *Trans. Am. Soc. Mech. Engrs.* **73**, 183 (1951).

22. Jenckel, E., and Huhn, H., *Kolloid-Z.* **159**, 118 (1958).

23. DeBruyne, N. A., *J. Appl. Chem.* **6**, 303 (1956).

24. Hofrichter, C. H., and McLaren, A. D., *Ind. Eng. Chem.* **40**, 329 (1948).

25. McLaren, A. D., and Seiler, C. J., *J. Polymer Sci.* **4**, 63(1949).

26. Voyutskii, S. S., Shapovalova, A. I., and Pisarenko, A. P., *Kolloid. Zhur.* **19**, 274 (1957).

27. Krotova, N. A., Kirillova, Yu. M., and Deryagin, B. V., *Zhur. Fiz. Khim.* **30**, 1921 (1956).

28. Snoddon, W. J., *Am. Soc. Testing Materials Spec. Tech. Publ. No.* **201**, 73 (1957).

29. Moser, F., and Knoell, S. S., *Am. Soc. Testing Materials Bull. No.* **227**, 60 (1958).

30. Sheridan, M. L., and Merriman, H. R., *Am. Soc. Testing Materials Spec. Tech. Publ. No.* **201**, 33 (1957).

31. Black, J. M., and Blomquist, R. F., *Adhesives Age* **2**, No. 6, 27 (1959).

32. Raraty, L. E., and Tabor, D., *Proc. Roy. Soc.* A**245**, 184 (1958).

33. Lacks, H., Quatinetz, M., and Freiberger, A., *Am. Soc. Testing Materials Bull. No.* **224**, 48 (1957).

34. Krotova, N. A., *Kauchuk i Rezina* **1940**, No. 8, 28.

35. Dietz, A. G. H., Bockstruck, H. N., and Epstein, G., *Am. Soc. Testing Materials Spec. Tech. Publ. No.* **138**, 40 (1952).

36. Desai, M. B., and McGarry, F. J., *Am. Soc. Testing Materials Bull. No.* **239**, 76 (1959).

CHAPTER 9

Tests

§99. THE NUMBER of tests suggested and adopted for adjudging adhints is so great that a book longer than "The Science of Adhesive Joints" would be needed to describe them adequately. Unfortunately, hardly any of these tests affords results having general significance. If a definite treament is applied to several supposedly identical joints and a range of values is obtained, we may conclude that also other joints made in the same manner and subjected to an identical treatment will give values of a similar magnitude. This, of course, is an important piece of information whenever joints are used. But such tests do not enable us to make any prediction as to the behavior of slightly different adhints or of identical adhints treated in a slightly different way, see §82. Prediction is predicated on understanding.

Because of the frankly empirical nature of the usual tests and because they are easily found in the publications of the American Society for Testing Materials, as British Standard Specifications and so on, they are not described in this book. In this chapter, a few examples of less common methods of testing are outlined.

§100. A METHOD often used in rubber industry is the "pull-through" test. A straight length of a string (or cord, or rope) is embedded in a rubber mixture, the mixture is vulcanized, and the string is pulled out by a longitudinal force as indicated in Fig. 108. The external cylindrical surface of the rubber plug is firmly clamped. Obviously, the system is analogous to a cylindrical lap joint, §76. To derive an approximate theory of the test,[1] we refer to §69.2. If the reasoning leading to equation (97) is repeated for the present instance, in which h_0 is indefinite be-

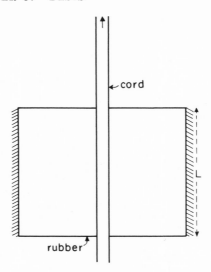

FIG. 108. A "pull-through" test.

cause the whole block of rubber corresponds to the adhesive in §69.2, we obtain equation

$$\frac{\partial^2 l_1}{\partial z^2} = \frac{2c l_1}{Er};$$
(125)

E is modulus of elasticity of the cord (assumed to be a Hookean solid), r is the radius of the cord [corresponding to δ in equation (97)] and c is the ratio of shear stress to displacement in the system; thus, shear stress acting in the cord-rubber interface is $c l_1$; the dimension of c is g./sec.^{2}.

Integration of equation (125) affords

$$l_1 = 2 A \cosh \lambda z = A (e^{\lambda z} + e^{-\lambda z}),$$
(126)

A being an arbitrary constant and $\lambda = (2c/Er)^{0.5}$. Since $f = E(\partial l_1/\partial z)$, see equation (94),

$$f = AE\lambda(e^{\lambda z} - e^{-\lambda z}) = 2AE\lambda \sinh \lambda z.$$
(127)

Thus,

$$f = E\lambda l_1 \tanh \lambda z.$$
(128)

Assume now that rupture starts when l_1 anywhere reaches the maximum possible value which we shall denote l_m. Let the corresponding stress be f_m. The greatest value of l_1 is reached first, naturally, at $z = L$, L being the length of the embedded part of the cord. Hence,

$$f_m = E\lambda l_m \tanh \lambda L. \tag{129}$$

This equation predicts that the force needed to pull a cord out of a rubber block is proportional to tanh of the embedded length. Figure 109 reproduces some experimental results.[1] Its ordinate is the above force (in lb. wt., multiply with 445 to obtain it in kilodynes) and the abscissa is L in eights of an inch (multiply by 0.3175 to have it in cm.). The curves really are similar to those of tanh. The material of the cord (brass-plated steel, cotton, a polyester of terephthalic acid, nylon, and a rayon) is marked at the curves.

It is interesting to note the contradiction between the assumptions made in this section and those of §69.2. There, the displacement at $z = 0$ was set equal to zero with the result that a finite unbalanced force seemed to act at this level. Here, force at $z = 0$ is assumed to be zero; consequently, a displacement equal to $2A$, see equation (126), seems to exist at the lower end of the cord where there is no force which could cause this displacement. A possible reason for this discrepancy is indicated in §69.2.

Because the maximum shear stress (at which still no failure occurs) is cl_1, it can be calculated from the data presented in Fig. 109. It proves to be little dependent on the nature of the cord and apparently does not contradict the idea that usually rubber gives way first.

§101.   A SIMILAR TEST[2] is illustrated in Fig. 110. A glass rod is embedded in a polymer disc. The rod is firmly clamped at both ends, and the disc is pushed up as indicated in the sketch. In these experiments, force F_m needed to achieve irreversible displacement of the disc was a linear function of the embedded length L when this varied from about 0.2 cm. to about 1.5 cm., for a rod 0.2 cm. in diameter. Extrapolation of F_m to

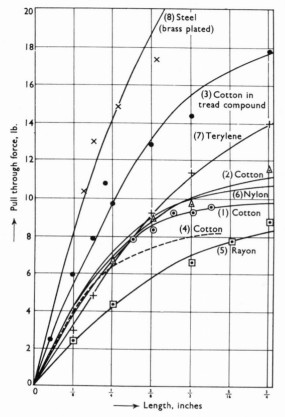

FIG. 109. Experimental results of a "pull-through" test. Abscissa: length of embedded cord in eights of an inch. Ordinate: maximum pulling force in lb. wt. From reference 1.

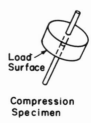

Compression
Specimen

FIG. 110. A "push-along" test. From reference 2.

$L = 0$ led to a considerable value of force; this was traced to the fact that the thickness of the disc was greater adjacent to the rod than further away because the resin wetted the glass and formed a meniscus which persisted also after curing. The value of L to which the preceding statements refer is that far from the rod.

If again, see equation (93), it is assumed that dF_m/dL is proportional to the maximum possible shear stress at the rod-disc boundary, this stress can readily be calculated. It is similar to the shear strength of the polymer in bulk for the instance of a cured epoxy resin but is unexpectedly small in the instance of a copolymer of styrene and esters of dibasic acids; thus we may conclude that a weak boundary layer exists along the glass-polyester interface; this layer was mentioned in §27.

A modification of the system depicted in Fig. 110 permits measurement of the traction required to break the glass-matrix bond in the direction perpendicular to the interface.[3] The principle of the method is indicated in Fig. 111. The plastic body has

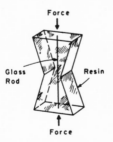

Fig 111. An adhesion test based on Poisson's contraction. From reference 3.

approximately the shape of an hourglass, and the glass filament is wholly embedded along its axis of cylindrical symmetry. When pressure is applied to the top and bottom surfaces of the composite body, the height of the latter decreases. Since stress is greater the smaller the horizontal cross section of the plastic body, the main part of this decrease occurs along the waist of the hourglass. Let the length (or height) of this waist be L before and $L - dL$ after compression. This axial contraction causes extension in the radial direction. If the initial radius of the filament is r_1 and its Poisson ratio is ν_1, then the filament will tend to have, at the waist, a radius equal to $r_1[1 + \nu_1(dL/L)]$. On the other hand, if Poisson's ratio of the matrix is ν_2, an axial hole of radius r_1 in the matrix will tend to have the radius $r_1[1 + \nu_2(dL/L)]$. The actual radius, as long as no rupture takes place, will be between these two magnitudes; thus, if $\nu_1 < \nu_2$, both the filament and the polymer will be forcibly extended in the radial direction (normally to the external pressure). The tendency of the filament to contract toward the axis and of the matrix away from this axis produces a stress along the radius, proportional to the difference $\nu_2 - \nu_1$. The magnitude of this stress, when failure occurs, is similar to the breaking stress calculated from the tests on the systems of Fig. 110.

§102.   DISCUSSION OF TESTS for the adherence of coatings does not belong in this monograph but three of the many suggested procedures for such tests are outlined here to show that the difficulty of measuring the true adhesion in the instance of coating is just as great as in the case of adhints.

Two of these procedures manifest some analogy with the tensile breaking of butt joints. In one,[4] the coating is removed by centrifugal force. For instance, the cylindrical surface of a bar can be coated and the bar rotated around its axis of cylindrical symmetry; when the rate of rotation is very great, the coating may fly off. In this arrangement, the so-called hoop stresses are operative; see, e.g., reference 5. Their nature may be explained as follows. Let the radius of the cylinder at rest be r_0; when the cylinder rotates, its radius increases because of centrifugal forces to, say, r_1. Consequently the circumference of the cylinder, that is the length of the coating-bar boundary increases from $2\pi r_0$ to $2\pi r_1$. Thus, the coating is elongated, and this elongation produces stresses resisting fruther elongation; they are the hoop stresses.

To simplify the system, assume that we rotate the cylinder around an axis perpendicular to its generatrix, see Fig. 112, and that the basis faces are coated. Obviously, no hoop stresses can appear in this arrangement but the stress pattern still is any-

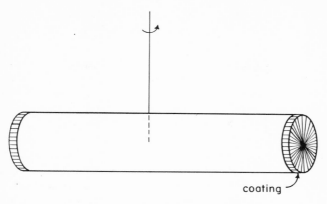

Fɪɢ. 112. Test of adhesion by centrifuging.

thing but simple. The centrifugal force on a slice, dl cm. thick, of the cylinder (cut normally to its axis and parallel to the axis of revolution) is $A\rho\omega^2 l \cdot dl$, if A is the area of the crosssection, ρ the density of the material, ω the angular velocity (in radians/ sec., the dimension of ω is sec.$^{-1}$), and l is the distance from the axis of revolution. Thus in the region near the bar -coating boundary where, because of surface roughness the planes characterized by l = const. pass partly through the adherend and partly through the coating, centrifugal stress $\rho\omega^2 l \cdot dl$ is greater in the denser material (usually in the bar) than in the less dense substance. Apparently, no calculation of this differential effect ever has been made.

When the bar depicted in Fig. 112 rotates, it elongates parallel to the cylinder axis; this elongation must be accompanied by Poisson's contraction of the radius. An identical effect must occur in the coating. Since the moduli of elasticity and the Poisson ratios of the two materials are different, stresses analogous to those considered in §67 must exist near the interface. Thus, as far as simplicity of interpretation is concerned, centrifugal force offers no advantage compared to tensile force on butt joints.

Analogous remarks apply to the "bullet method."[6] In this, the central part of a basis of a cylinder is coated, and the cylinder is shot in the direction of its axis at a target which essentially is a ring normal to the direction of the movement. The internal diameter of the ring is greater than that of the coated patch but smaller than that of the cylinder. Thus the cylinder is stopped by the ring but the coating, because of inertia, tends to continue its flight. If the thickness of the coating is h, the pressure tending to remove the coating, at a first approximation, is $\rho h j_{max}$, if j_{max} is the maximum deceleration (cm./sec.^{2}) achieved during impact and ρ is the density of the coating. However, this approximation presumably is a crude one. When the periphery of the bullet basis is stopped by the ring, the center (which is coated) continues to advance and then must vibrate about the equilibrium position; it is not known what stresses exist during these vibrations but evidently they are different from $\rho h j_{max}$.

The third method uses bursting. In a rigid plate a hole is drilled, see Fig. 113. The hole is plugged with an easily removable

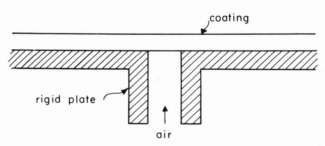

FIG. 113. Test of adhesion by bursting.

material such as an amalgam or a water-soluble plastic, so that the surface of the plug and the surface of the plate form one plane. Then plate + plug is coated (the thickness of the coating is exaggerated in the figure), the plug is removed (for instance, by dissolving it in water) without hurting the film, and the underside of the film is connected with a reservoir of compressed air (or mercury). Air pressure P at which the coating is torn off is supposed to be a measure of adhesion between coating and plate. In a more elaborate arrangement,[7] only a rectangular strip of the coating is permitted to bulge out and to rupture.

The actual stress causing failure seems to be a function of
P and of several mechanical and geometrical properties of the
coating membrane and, in all probability, has no connection
with the molecular attraction between plate and coating. If,
at a first approximation, the membrane before bursting may be
treated as a part of a spherical surface, it has a constant radius
of curvature, say R, and the tension in the membrane then is
0.5 PR g./sec.^{2}, see §46. Real membranes do not have a constant
curvature and their R varies from center to periphery according
to a law which depends on the stiffness of the membrane. If, for
instance, the membrane is so flexible that the energy associated
with its bending is small compared with that associated with
stretching, then the tensile stress at the boundary of the hole
is[8] $f = 0.328 \ (EP^2a^2/h^2)^{1/3}$, E is modulus of elasticity, a radius,
and h thickness of the membrane. As is apparent from Fig. 114,

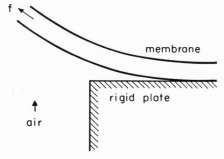

FIG. 114. Peeling effect in the bursting test.

stress f causes peeling and, thus, should be treated according
to the pattern of §77. Peeling of a circular membrane is, in one
respect, simpler than that of a long ribbon because the edge
stresses depicted in Fig. 89 do not exist; on the other hand, it
is less predictable because the effective angle of peeling depends
on the stiffness and the diameter of the membrane; thus an
additional variable is introduced.

§103.   ALL TESTS so far described in this chapter involve
destruction of the specimen. It is clear that nondestructive
tests would be very valuable; we would like to be able, by exam-

ining a completed adhint, to predict whether it will stand up to the use intended for it.

The nondestructive tests so far suggested, and so far as they are known to the present author, are based on the resonance properties of the adhint. The simplest test consists in hitting a metal-adhesive-metal joint with "a large coin"[9] or another solid; a sound adhint gives forth a sonorous, and a faulty one, a dull sound. Evidently, the difference corresponds to that between a whole and a slightly cracked glass vessel.

More ambitious tests utilize supersonic vibrations. In §68, equations are given for calculating the modulus of elasticity E of adhesive films in butt joints. If these films are incomplete, that is contain voids, their over-all E may be expected to be smaller than that of a sound film. On the other hand, voids would depress the strength of adhints. Thus we may expect, in a series of supposedly identical adhints, breaking stress to increase with the value of E; hence, by measuring E it would be possible to predict the value of the rupture stress. This method was successfully used in some systems[10] but was not always sufficiently sensitive.[11]

The above procedure involves comparing the adhint with an adherend bar of the double length; obviously this requirement in many instances renders the method unsuitable for production control. A method, in which production adhints are compared with a perfect adhint of the identical type rather than with a solid piece of the adherend material, is easier to apply.[12, 13] A vibrating barium titanate plate is placed on a perfect joint and the mode of its vibration is observed on the screen of an oscilloscope. Then the plate is brought in contact with an adhint of unknown quality; if a marked change occurs in the oscillogram, the joint under test is not perfect. If a series of adhints of different degrees of perfection is available, the instrument (in which a galvanometer is substituted for the oscilloscope) can be calibrated with their help.

In another modification[14] one piezoelectric plate is pressed against one side of an adhint and another, identical, plate against the opposite side. The first plate vibrates, and the second picks up the vibrations and transforms them into electric pulses. If the regions of bad bonding are large in comparison with the wavelength of the vibrations, the second plate (i.e., "the receiver") emits weak signals only. If these regions are small, the transmission of vibrations is almost as good as when there are no defective areas; in these instances another effect can be utilized to detect flaws, namely the retardation of the arrival of the signals (sent out by the first plate) at the receiver. The procedure was not sufficiently sensitive; even voids of 1 cm. in diameter could not be safely detected unless the adhint was strained so that the adhesive film was extended by, for instance, 10%.

REFERENCES

1. Wood, J. O., *Trans. Inst. Rubber Ind.* **32**, 1 (1956).
2. McGarry, F. J., *Am. Soc. Testing Materials Bull. No.* **235**, 63 (1959).
3. Mooney, R. D., and McGarry, F. J., *14th Ann. Conf., Reinforced Plastics Div., Soc. Plastics Ind.* 12-E-1 (1959).
4. Malloy, A. M., Soller, W., and Roberts, A. G., *Paint, Oil Chem. Rev.* **116**, No. 18, 14; No. 19, 26 (1953); *Chem. Abstr.* **48**, 3042 (1954).
5. Beams, J. W., Breazeale, J. B., and Bart, W. L., *Phys. Rev.* **100**, 1657 (1955).
6. May, W. D., Smith, N. D. P., and Snow, C. I., *Trans. Inst. Met. Finishing* **34**, No. 9 (1957); *Nature* **179**, 494 (1957).
7. Dannenberg, H., *J. Polymer Sci.* **33**, 509 (1958).
8. Timoshenko, S., and Woinowsky-Krieger, S. "Theory of Plates and Shells," p. 404. McGraw-Hill, New York, 1959.
9. Noton, R. B., *Aluminium* **35**, 266 (1959).
10. Dietz, A. G. H., Bockstruck, H. N., and Epstein, G., *Am. Soc. Testing Materials Spec. Tech. Publ. No.* **138**, 40 (1952).
11. Tapp, P. F., Broodo, A., Horn, C. E., and Castner, S. V., *Aircraft Eng.* **29**, 350 (1957).
12. Arnold, J. S., *Am. Soc. Testing Materials Spec. Tech. Publ. No.* **201**, 83 (1957).
13. Schijve, J., *Aircraft Eng.* **30**, 269 (1958).
14. Heughan, D. M., and Sproule, D. O., *Trans. Inst. Rubber Ind.* **29**, 255 (1953).

CHAPTER 10

Summary for the Practical Man

§104. IF A SERIES OF JOINTS has satisfactory strength, no study of the materials or processes used is indicated for the practical man. If, however, joints do not perform satisfactorily, the cause of the weakness must be found and removed. In this search, the first question to be answered is that of the location of the failure. Rupture can occur in an adherend, the adhesive, or in a weak boundary layer. In many instances simple visual inspection of the fracture faces permits a decision as to where the adhint fractured. When this inspection proves inconclusive, the following remarks may be of help.

I. A weak boundary layer should aways be suspected if (a) joint strength appears to be too small to be accounted for by equation (130), §105, and (b) fracture surface is situated very near to the surface of the adherend. Both (a) and (b) are needed.

II. If a material used as adhesive gives rise to poor joints with very different adherends (such as glass, aluminum, stainless steel, galenite), we may assume that weak boundary layers form and that the substances finally present in these layers originally were a part of the adhesive.

III. If an adherend gives rise to poor joints with very different adhesives (low-melting alloys, adhesionable polyethylene, polyesters, and so on) which can be successfully used with other solids, we may assume that the surface of the adherend carries an inherent weak boundary layer.

If adherend A_1 affords weak joints with adhesive a_1 while it can be glued well with other adhesives and while a_1 can be used for other adherends, then only the above rule No. I can be helpful in estimating the probability of a weak zone at the interface of A_1 and a_1.

Suppose that the presence of a weak boundary layer has been made probable. Such a layer can originate in many ways and the remedy will vary with the origin.

1. The material of the weak zone comes from the surroundings. For the customary joints made in air, this means that air remains trapped along the adherend-adhesive interface. Incomplete wetting is the most common reason for residual air, see §§22 to 23. The degree of wetting should be determined, and it should be possible to achieve an improvement in the joint strength by using an adhesive which perfectly wets the solid or by assembling joints in a vacuum.

2. The material of the weak zone comes from the adhesive. This usually can be recognized as described in II above. The remedy is to remove the deleterious ingredients by fractional precipitation, extraction, or another suitable procedure. For an example see §48.

3. The material of the weak zone comes from the adherend. This is the case outlined in III above. Cleaning of the adherend surface, see §§27 and 28, or extraction of the adherend with solvents may be attempted.

4. The weak boundary layer forms in an interaction between the adhesive and the environment: thus, if the adhesive is subjected to an excessive temperature during its application, oxidation by atmospheric oxygen may occur and may, because of special circumstances, be more pronounced near the adherend-adhesive interface. The effects of this kind would be eliminated by producing the adhint in different surroundings (e.g., nitrogen gas) and, if a change in the environment really improves the strength, it is proved that the weak zone has the origin defined in this paragraph.

5. The weak boundary layer forms in an interaction between the adherend and the environment: thus a brittle oxide of copper is sometimes produced by heating the metal during the formation of the joint. Detection and prevention of this ill would be performed as outlined in the preceding paragraph.

6. The weak boundary layer forms in a reaction between the adherend and the adhesive. Examples: wood weakened by alka-

line glue, see §51, and copper sulfide at the interface between
brass and rubber, §49. The number of reactions which can give
rise to such layers is very great and, at present, no general in-
struction can be formulated as to how to find the culprit.

7. All three phases (i.e., air, adherend, and adhesive) participate in the formation of a zone of weakness. For an example
see §51. This type is detected by proving that change of only
one of the components is sufficient to avoid weak joints; thus
substitution of aluminum for copper, or of another adhesive for
that showing the effect, or of nitrogen for air prevented deterioration of the interfacial layer in the above instance. The remedy is
to alter one of the three components.

§105. IF NO WEAK BOUNDARY is present, the adhint breaks
in the adherend or in the adhesive. In the first case, the science
of adhesive joints is not involved. If the adhesive breaks, we wish
to utilize as much as possible of its inherent strength, that is we
aspire to have rupture stresses of adhints about as great as or
greater than those of the adhesive in bulk. Our success depends
on equation

$$\frac{f_m}{f_M} = \frac{\beta_0}{\alpha\beta} \cdot \frac{\xi - \beta s}{\xi - \beta_0 s_0} \tag{130}$$

already given in §82. The greater the ratio f_m/f_M, the better the
utilization of the adhesive.

To reduce the macroscopical stress concentration factor α to
a value not much greater than its minimum magnitude (i.e.,
unity) the rheological properties of adherend and adhesive
should be as similar as feasible. If neither the adhesive nor the
adherend can be changed, we may sometimes lower the value of
α by inserting an intermediate layer (a primer) between the two;
the material of this layer should have a modulus of elasticity
intermediate between those of the adherend and the cement.
Another possibility is to alter the design of the adhint; the magnitude of α in adhints of various types is treated in Chapter VII.

Ratio f_m/f_M is greater the smaller the shrinkage stress s. This
can be reduced by using adhesives which have almost identical
densities before and after setting (assuming, as usually is the

case, that the density of the adherends remains practically constant during setting). When this cannot be done, again a primer coat which shrinks more than the adherends and less than the adhesive would be helpful. By a skillful design it should be possible in some instances to buttress f_m by shrinkage stresses; if, for instance, the adhint is made in such a manner that it is strained in compression during use, the sign of s would be reversed and f_m would be greater the greater s. As a rule, s is less the thinner the cement film; thus, the effect of shrinkage stress on f_m can be influenced by the thinness of the joint.

To make β small, we should try to avoid formation of air bubbles and analogous flaws during setting and to remove (for instance, by squeezing the excess cement out) those bubbles etc. which are bound to appear during the application of the adhesive. Since β is greater the thicker the "glue line," the adherends should be brought together as closely as feasible.

Finally, ξ itself may be smaller in the adhint than in the bulk, if, for instance, polymerization or cross-linking of the adhesive *in situ* resulted in a degree of polymerization or type of cross-linking less favorable than those in the bulk sample.

§106.   A survey of the two preceding paragraphs in the form of a table may be welcome. The low strength of an adhint may be due to

I. A weak boundary layer originating from:
1. the surroundings
2. the adhesive
3. the adherend
4. the adhesive and the surroundings
5. the adherend and the surroundings
6. the adherend and the adhesive
7. the adherend, the adhesive, and the surroundings.

II. Low breaking stress of the adhesive because of:
1. deterioration of the adhesive material
2. stress concentrations
3. shrinkage stresses
4. bad flaws in the adhesive

§107. In §§104 to 106 the diagnosis and the therapeutics of unsatisfactory adhints were described. A related problem consists in selecting the best adhesive for a given pair of adherends. It also comprises two parts, one dealing with the avoidance of weak boundary layers and the other, with minimizing stress concentrations.

The procedure to adopt in avoiding improper (§15) joints depends on how much effort can be spent on purifying the materials employed. It is clear that a household cement will be applied to relatively dirty solids; therefore, an adhesive sensitive to impurities cannot be chosen. Thus, polyethylenes are practically insoluble in all common solvents and, correspondingly, are (in the solid state) very poor solvents themselves; in other words, almost any fluid which comes in contact with polyethylene remains on its surface and thus may constitute a weak boundary layer. Hence, polyethylenes are not suitable as household cements. An identical remark applies to other substances which have a low degree of miscibility with matter (such as finger grease) which is likely to be present on the solids to be glued.

The usual household cements are solutions of several ingredients in a powerful solvent. When they are placed on a solid whose surface is contaminated with finger grease and similar common impurities, these impurities are dissolved by the solvent and thus distributed among the other components. The miscibility of these components with each other and with finger grease is so good that no separation in distinct phases occurs and, consequently, no weak boundary layer can form.

At the opposite extreme are the adhesives designed for a specific application of great responsibility. The adherends in these instances can be thoroughly prepared for the application, and the first column of the table in §106 may be used for systematic removal of the possible sources of a weak zone.

As far as stress concentrations are concerned, an adhesive very similar to the adherends in its rheological behavior would be the ideal choice; the magnitude of the α factor, §105, would not be much greater than unity in such a combination. When also the heat expansions of adherends and cement are comparable, the shrinkage stresses of thermal origin also will be small. A third favorable similarity would be that in the chemical resistance of the two materials; if, for instance, one of these does, and the other does not, swell in humid atmosphere, every change of relative humidity of the atmosphere will cause stresses near the adherend-adhesive boundary. Thus the adhesive should be as like the adherends in all respects as can be achieved under the circumstances.

The rule formulated in the preceding sentence is valueless when the two adherends are different, such as a metal and a rubber. Probably, adhesives having mechanical properties halfway between those of the two adherends would be most suitable in these combinations. Thus, if the two adherends have moduli of elasticity E_1 and E_2, total relative elongations $(\Delta l/l)_1$ and $(\Delta l/l)_2$, etc., then an adhesive whose modulus is near $0.5(E_1 + E_2)$ and the total relative elongation is near $0.5[(\Delta l/l)_1 + (\Delta l/l)_2]$ would be indicated (if all its other properties fit the case). Unfortunately, no experimental check of this deduction is known to the author.

The reasoning of this section, so far, implies that the final strength of the adhint, §54, is the only, or at least the main, property the user is interested in. This implication is incorrect in numberless instances. Often any final strength above a modest minimum is satisfactory but some other properties are critical. Thus a "quick grab" or tack, see Chapter IV, is the first consideration in manufacturing cardboard boxes. In other applications, none of the mechanical or rheological properties is of primary importance: the cement may be weak but must be transparent, or may be weak but must not evolve gases or vapors. Selection of the best cement for the two last-named systems presumably will be better helped by a book on adhesives than by a monograph on adhints.

Author Index

Numbers in parentheses are reference numbers and indicate that an author's work is referred to although his name is not cited in the text. Numbers in italics show the page on which the complete reference is listed.

Subject Index